X PLANES

secret planes and secret missions

X PLANES

HarperCollinsPublishers

HarperCollins*Publishers*
77-85 Fulham Palace Road
Hammersmith
London W6 8JB

First published by HarperCollins*Publishers* 2000

1 3 5 7 9 10 8 6 4 2

© David Oliver and Mike Ryan 2000

ISBN 0 00 472461 5

Design: Rod Teasdale

Printed in Great Britain by Scotprint

CONTENTS

INTRODUCTION 6

CHAPTER ONE
SKUNKS AND PHANTOMS 10

CHAPTER TWO
UP AND AWAY 24

CHAPTER THREE
FORCE MULTIPLIER 40

CHAPTER FOUR
BLACK HOLES 58

CHAPTER FIVE
NOW YOU SEE IT, NOW YOU DON'T 80

CHAPTER SIX
BEHIND THE LINES 102

CHAPTER SEVEN
FASHION FIGHTERS 124

CHAPTER EIGHT
DOODLEBUGS TO ROBOBUGS 142

CHAPTER NINE
SILVER BULLETS 160

A s aviation enters its second century, now is the time to discover where it has come from, and where it is going.

The technology which made man's first flight possible was driven by the invention of the internal combustion engine at the end of the previous century. It was then more than 30 years before a new practical form of propulsion, the jet engine, was used to power aircraft and it continues to do so to the present day. Along the way, the rocket engine, ramjet and pulsejet or combinations of all three, have been experimented with, with varying degrees of success.

The amazing pace of aerospace development has been accelerated by conflict. During World War One, the aircraft became a weapon. By the end of World War Two, air power had the ability to annihilate whole cities with one bomb, and during the longest war of the 20th century - the Cold War - the opposing superpowers spent virtually unlimited defence budgets on keeping one step ahead of the other.

Above: Force multiplier: Boeing's giant C-17

Inspired by advanced German aviation technology that was brought to a halt in 1945, the victorious Allies, which then included the Soviet Union, made major strides in military aviation development in the immediate post-war era. The swept wings of US F-86 Sabre fighters, SAC' B-47 *Stratojet* bombers and the Soviet MiG-15 were all designed using captured German data. Early American missile and drone technology was based on the V-1 flying bomb.

When the Iron Curtain fell in Europe, the development of many advanced jet fighters, bombers, surveillance platforms, helicopters and unmanned aircraft, went 'Black' and ultra secret flight test centres in the United States and the Soviet Union became cauldrons of technological excellence, attracting the best brains from ever more diverse disciplines. Whereas the first heavier-than-air flying machines depended solely on the development of the piston-engine, aerospace technology in the second half of the 20th century was almost wholly dependent on the growth of the computer.

While 'Black' programmes, that did not exist, were flight tested at 'Black Holes', that were not there, it was not only potential enemies that were kept in the dark. On many occasions, the US and Soviet governments were completely unaware of what billions of dollars and roubles were being spent on at any one time, and the superpowers' NATO and WarPac allies would be some of the last to be made aware that any major push at the boundaries of technology was in the offing.

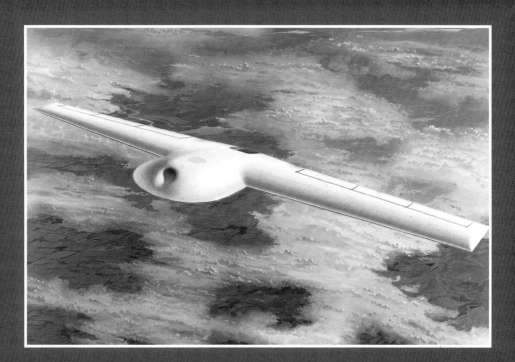

Above: 'Dark Star' is an unmanned reconnaissance platform, but a prototype of the same name
has been heard having radio conversations with chase aircraft.

When funds for covert military aircraft development was almost unrestricted, the dreams of many German designers and engineers became realities, from flying wings to hypersonic interceptors. The sheer number of innovative projects that were being worked on by the German aviation industry, during the desperate last months before it faced destruction and ruin, was unprecedented. The prospect of defeat was an obvious spur to technological creativity, but time was not on Germany's side.

As the Allies smashed their way through a devastated Third Reich in 1945, futuristic projects were discovered in farm barns, salt mines and man-made caves. Many were not recognised for what they were and merely destroyed on the spot. How many German 'dream-machines' were lost forever will never be known.

It did not take long for American, British and Soviet experts to recognise the value of these discoveries and a three-way race was on to secure them. Eastern Germany proved to be a treasure-trove that fell under Soviet

Above: The world's most advanced 'scale model aircraft': the remotely controlled X-36 may be followed by full-size unmanned fighter planes.

control in 1946. Peenemunde was the prize, although most of its scientists had made their way to the West and the safety of Operation *Paperclip*. The island airfield would become a WarPac fighter base in the frontline of the Cold War until German reunification in 1990.

When East faced West, each had confidence that its defences were superior and the long-running nuclear chess game was played out to checkmate by the 1970s. Superior computer and microchip technology, ever escalating defence budgets and its relentless quest for stealth, supercruise, and finally the 'Star Wars' Strategic Defense Initiative (SDI), enabled the United States to force the Soviet Union to throw in the towel without a shot being fired by the end of the 1980s.

Since the end of the Cold War, air forces and aerospace industries in the United States, and elsewhere, have 'downsized and rationalised' leaving them leaner and outwardly highly cost-conscious. Expensive programmes at the cutting edge of known aerospace technologies now have to be 'partnerships' with acceptable 'green and friendly' agencies such as NASA, or as part of a multinational consortium. Anything overtly 'military' is not

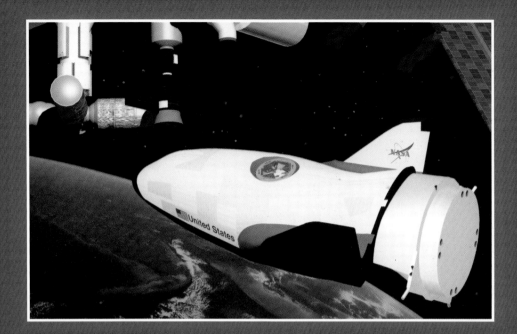

Above: NASA artwork depicts a crew shuttle poised to return
to earth from the space station.

However, this situation has played into the hands of the 'Black' fraternity, which still manages to thrive and proper in the shadows. With ever more capable computers, virtual projects can be designed, built and flown with very few personnel involved. Components, which can be small and seemingly insignificant, are produced at a number of remote facilities and only transported to a central site for final assembly of the air vehicle or propulsion system, another ploy used by German aircraft manufacturers at the end of World War Two.

The new 'enemy' of the 21st century that has to be defeated by present and future 'Black' programmes is technology itself. In the same way that a climber has go on conquering ever higher mountains, 'because they are there', aerospace scientists and engineers of the new millennium will continue to probe further and further into the unknown. The 'Black' philosophy is, 'if we don't do it, someone else will'.

As the 100th anniversary of man's first flight approaches, future aerospace frontiers to the digitised battlefield will be crossed using 'smart' materials, 'thinking' flight control systems, virtual pilots, micro-electromechanical systems (MEMS), solid-state lasers - and plasma-spikes.

Skunk Works

Skunk Works
Skunk Works

When project manager Clarence L 'Kelly' Johnson brought together a hand-picked team of Lockheed engineers and manufacturing personnel in 1943 at the company's Burbank facility, each team member was cautioned that the design and manufacture of a new jet fighter must be carried out in strict secrecy. No one was to discuss the project outside the team.

This was the second year of the United States' involvement in World War Two and the secret aircraft that Lockheed was working on was the XP-80, later known as the *Shooting Star*.

Legend has it that the name of this undercover organisation came from Al Capp's famous cartoon strip 'Li'l Abner' which depicted a mysterious place deep in the forest called the 'Skonk Works' where 'moonshine' was brewed from assorted ingredients - including skunks. The name evolved into the Skunk Works which, 50 years later, Lockheed registered as a trademark.

Right: The Skunk Works logo is now a Lockheed Martin trademark.

When the first prototype Shooting Star was designed and built, it was the responsibility of the Lockheed Advanced Aeronautics Company. It was only five years after the first low-wing monoplane fighter with retractable landing gear, the P-36, had entered USAAF service, when the go-ahead was given for the XP-80. Designed around the British Halford H-1 turbojet engine, the *Shooting Star* took only 143 days from 'pencil to flight'. The completed prototype was transported to the remote Muroc Army Air Field, later Edwards Air Force Base, for its first flight on 8 January 1944.

Other products of the Burbank Skunk Works included the swept-wing XF-90 deep penetration fighter and the US Navy's XFV-1 vertical take-off and landing (VTOL) turboprop-powered fighter. Neither went into production. However, by 1953, 'Kelly' Johnson had become Lockheed's chief engineer and was installed in a new custom-built Skunk Works at a remote location at Palmdale, California, 35 miles north of Burbank.

This move coincided with the continuing work of his team on another advanced fighter project, the supersonic XF-104. Despite limited service with the USAF, more than 2,500 of the Mach 2.0 *Starfighter*, which made its first flight at Edwards AFB on 4 March 1954, were built in Europe, Canada and Japan.

A Skunk Works' milestone, not just for the extreme secrecy which surrounded the project but because, from design to manufacture, it was handled by Johnson's team, was Project *Aquatone*, better known to the outside world as the U-2, a high-altitude reconnaissance aircraft funded by the Central Intelligence Agency (CIA). The first prototype, 'Article 341', was moved from the Skunk Works at Burbank to Area 51 at Groom Lake in a USAF C-

Above: The ultra secret *Have Blue* served as a technology demonstrator for the F-117A 'Stealth' fighter.

Above: The F-117A Nighthawk production line at the Burbank Skunk Works.

first 'stealth' aircraft. Its Pratt & Whitney J58 bypass turbojets used special JP4 fuel to give them an after-burning thrust rating of 32,500lb.

The first A-12 was transported by trailer from Burbank on 26 February 1962 arriving safely at Area 51, two days later. On 26 April, Lockheed test pilot Lou Schalk took the aircraft into the air for the first time. Although only 10 A-12 aircraft were constructed for the CIA, known as the *Cygnus*, including a two-seater code-named *Goose*, three more airframes were completed as dedicated single-seat interceptor fighters.

During December 1960, a separate project group was organised in the Skunk Works, running independently of the A-12 team. The entire forward fuselage forebody of an A-12 would be modified to create a Mach 3.2 interceptor. Originally designated AF-12, the aircraft was equipped with the Hughes AN/ASG-18 pulse Doppler radar and the AIM-47 missile system, originally intended for the cancelled North American F-108 *Rapier*.

Following Air Force approval of the project, the prototype, now designated YF-12A, was fitted with a revised nose configuration and a large ventral folding fin to improve stability at high speed. On 7 August 1963, several weeks after being moved to Groom Lake, Jim Eastham climbed aboard the interceptor prototype, and took

Above: The last 'Black' aircraft built at Burbank was the F-117A which remained 'hidden' for a decade.

Above: Lockheed A-12A 60-6937, one of a pair later used for high-speed trials by NASA, had flown spy missions over North Vietnam in 1967/8.

it for its first flight, a flight he would later modestly describe as a 'typical production test flight'.

However, the F-12A was never ordered into production and the record-breaking aircraft were used for high-speed research until 1979. A bomber version of the A-12, designated the RB-12, also reached the mock-up stage, but this would prove to be stillborn, as it represented too much of a threat to the highly political North American XB-70A *Valkyrie*.

Other A-12 aircraft were converted to 'mother' aircraft as part of project *Tagboard*. In October 1962, Johnson was asked by the CIA to design a supersonic drone that could be mated with an A-12. The reason was the US Government's decision to discontinue covert Soviet Union overflights, following the Gary Powers shoot-down.

By 1963 the overall configuration for the Q-12 and its launch platform — two modified A-12s, designated 'M' for Mother-12 — were nearing completion. The Q-12 became the 'D' for Daughter-21.

The 11,000 lb D-21 was supported on the M-21 by a single, dorsally-mounted pylon. The mothership's pilot

Above: A vision of a future high-tech battlefield scenario published by the Skunk Works shows an unknown stealthy reconnaissance platform in the centre - which may be an as yet unrevealed 'Black' programme.

navigation system (INS), the D-21 would fly a pre-programmed flight profile with camera on/off points to produce the perfect photo-recce sortie. Having completed its camera run, the drone's INS system then sent signals to the auto-pilot system to descend to a predetermined film collection point. The entire unit containing INS, camera and film, was then ejected at 60,000ft and Mach 1.67 and parachuted towards the ocean. As the drone continued its descent, it was blown apart by a barometrically activated explosive charge.

On 22 December the first D-21/M-21 flight took place from Area 51 but on a subsequent test flight the D-21 collided with the Mothership during separation, killing one of the M-21 crew.

Tagboard was delayed for a year whilst a new launch system was developed. Code-named *Senior Bowl*, this involved the drone being launched from

Above: Four of the Skunk works most famous products, clockwise - the F-117A, F-36 JSF, U-2R and SR-71 Balckbird.

the under-wing pylons of two modified B-52Hs and although four operational overflights over China were attempted, with only limited success between 1969 and early 1971, *Senior Bowl* was cancelled on 15 July 1971.

While working on *Oxcart*, 'Kelly' Johnson had mentioned the possibility of producing a reconnaissance/strike variant for the Air Force. By the end of April 1962, two different mock-ups were under construction at the Skunk Works referred to as the R-12 and RS-12. On 18 February 1963, Lockheed received authority to build six R-12 aircraft known as Project *Senior Crown* later designated SR-71 by the Air Force, with the understanding that 25 aircraft would be ordered.

Above: The prototype X-35A Joint Strike Fighter (JSF) being assembled in the Palmdale alongside the Skunk Works logo.

The prototype SR-71A, was delivered from Burbank to Air Force Plant 42, at Palmdale, for final assembly on October 29 1964. With two J58s installed, Chief Test Pilot Bob Gilliland got airborne on 25 December from runway 25 at Palmdale, with an empty back seat, the Reconnaissance Systems Officer's (RSO) position, for safety reasons. During the flight he reached an altitude of 50,000ft (15,240m) and a speed of Mach 1.5.

The SR-71 was one of the Skunk Works' most successful projects that served with the USAF over the world's hot-spots for more than three decades.

In 1972, Ben Rich was appointed President of Advanced Development Projects (APD) paving the way for 'Kelly' Johnson's retirement in 1975, although he was retained as a senior advisor. He died in 1990.

Throughout the 1960s and 1970s during the height of the Cold War with the Soviet Union, the Skunk Works' main preoccupation remained with reconnaissance aircraft. However, Lockheed's advanced X-27 *Lancer* was one of the facility's few failures. Launched in 1971 as a private venture, and aimed at the USAF in competition with General Dynamic's YF-16, and later as a replacement for NATO's F-104G, the *Lancer* project was cancelled in August 1973 due to lack of interest.

Above: The logos on the tail-fins of the X-33 Venture Star, a next generation Reusable Launch Vehicle (RLV) shows that it is being built at the Skunk Works.

Cancellation of the X-27 left a void at the Skunk Works in the mid-1970s and apart from upgrades of the U-2 and SR-71, production at Palmdale virtually ground to a halt. The Lockheed company was also at a low ebb when in 1974 the US Defense Advanced Research Projects Agency (DARPA) sent out a request for research into a low observable (LO) fighter project.

The Skunk Works already had considerable experience of stealth technology which had been applied to the A-12/SR-71 family and Ben Rich was able to persuade the CIA to release some of the data, and the cash-strapped Lockheed Board to finance the study.

Rich's team, which included retired mathematician Bill Schroader, came up with an angular concept that would fragment and scatter radar returns better than any other shape. The investment paid off and in April 1976, Lockheed was selected to construct a new 'stealth' aircraft code-named *Have Blue*.

On 1 December 1977, the first of two prism-shaped technology demonstrators took to the air at Area 51. *Have Blue* Article 1001 made 36 successful test flights before being lost when it stalled on landing on 4 May 1978. Article 1002, which first flew on 20 July 1978, completed a further 52 test flights before the programme was successfully completed a year later.

Above: Much of the F-22 Raptor's highly classified stealth technology was developed at the Palmdale Skunk Works.

Almost immediately, the USAF awarded Lockheed a contract to design and build 20 LO subsonic attack aircraft under project *Senior Trend*. The 'stealth' fighter had arrived.

Again Ben Rich was responsible for the team which designed, hand-built and flew the prototype F-117A in less than three years, but the existence of the Air Force's first stealth fighter would not be officially revealed until 1988 by which time 51 aircraft had left the Burbank Skunk Works' production line.

Above: Major sections of the YF-22 were built at three separate locations and assembled at the Palmdale Skunk Works.

The F-117A *Nighthawk* was the last 'Black' aircraft to be built at Burbank; all future projects would be designed and assembled at Palmdale. Project *Senior Trend* was also the last 'Black' Skunk Works programme to be revealed to date.

However, the cutting edge of aerospace technology remains the Skunk Works' *raison d'être*. Research and development of the Lockheed Martin F-22 *Raptor*, and X-35 Joint Strike Fighter (JSF) is being carried out at Palmdale, which is also heavily involved in space technology and unmanned aerial vehicles (UAV).

The Lockheed Martin/Boeing *DarkStar* was an ultra-stealthy, flying-wing, high-altitude, battlefield surveillance UAV that made its first flight in 1966. However, following the loss of the prototype at Edwards AFB and escalating costs, the project was cancelled in 1999 but the technology will not be wasted.

A joint USAF/NASA programme, the advanced X-44A, a tailless research aircraft with three-dimensional thrust-vectoring coupled with advanced flight controls, is being developed at the Skunk Works as part of the Air Force's Future Aircraft Technology Enhancement (FATE) programme.

In 1996, the Skunk Works was selected to lead a multi-industry team to develop the next generation Single-stage-to-Orbit Reusable Launch Vehicle (RLV), the X-33 *Venture Star*, which is being built in the former B-1B Air Force Plant at Palmdale. It will be powered by linear aerospike rocket motors, an experimental version of which has been built at the Skunk Works and mounted on a NASA SR-71 for flight testing. A sub-scale X-33 demonstrator is scheduled to fly in 2001.

At the other end of the technology spectrum, another heavyweight contender is being developed by the Lockheed

Martin Skunk Works. The US Aerocraft, known as 'Superblimp', is being designed under a 'Black' programme with the British company Airship Technologies. Nearly 800 feet in length, the Aerocraft will resemble a giant conventional aircraft with four advanced turboprop tilt-rotor engines mounted on stub wings and a rigid cargo bay able to carry up to 500 tonnes of equipment such as 10 APCs or 1,500 troops.

The upper sections of the 'Superblimp' will comprise a helium-filled composite envelope which will enable the craft to take-off vertically using its tilt-rotors for propulsion before transitioning into the level flight mode and accelerating the Aerocraft to a cruising speed of some 150mph.

With a growing number of 'White' programs, known as *Big Safari* projects, and an unknown number of 'Black' programs being undertaken, the Skunk Works is expanding again. Current 'White' work includes fitting upgraded classified equipment to the U-2R fleet and C-130 EW, SIGINT and SOP aircraft.

At the end of the day, the Skunk Works is more than a facility, it is a team of highly talented and motivated aerospace designers, engineers and construction workers who are dedicated to innovation and excellence.

>>> Phantom Works <<<

McDonnell Douglas was one of the 'big four' of America's elite military aircraft manufacturers during the golden age of the 'Black' world of the 1970s. The appeal of making aircraft programmes 'Black' was readily apparent for both policy and technological reasons for McDonnell Douglas as well as Lockheed, General Dynamics and Northrop. Most classified aircraft programmes started out as relatively inexpensive research and development (R&D) programmes which meant that they were affordable at a time when the post-Vietnam cuts led to 'hollow' cuts if the decision-makers knew that something better was being developed as a 'Black' programme, as President Jimmy Carter did to the B-1A after learning of the 'Black' development of the B-2 bomber and stealth cruise missiles.

Above: The Phantom Works logo - NAMC stands for 'New Aircraft and Missile Products.'

In the Post-Vietnam era, American computer technology had moved far ahead of the Soviet Union and keeping advanced military programmes classified denied the Soviets not only knowledge needed for countermeasures, but led them to spend more of their research and development resources trying to cover all the options.

McDonnell Douglas of St Louis had teamed with General Dynamics for several 'Black' programmes that studied a wide range of advanced fighter concepts and modifications to existing fighters such as the F-16, F-15 and F-111. These advanced concepts included a conventional aircraft called '*Plain Jane*', a supersonic stealth configuration, a small inexpensive fighter called '*Bushwhacker*', a large fighter called '*Missiler*' that could carry long-range air-to-air missiles, and the highly stealthy all-wing fighter called '*Sneaky Pete*' which eventually evolved into the US Navy's short-lived A-12.

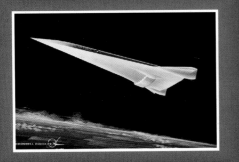

Above: A McDonnell concept of a hypersonic strategic reconnaissance aircraft based on the cancelled hypersonic X-30 National Aerospace Plane (NASP).

Named *Avenger II*, the deep 'Black' A-12 programme suffered from excessively high levels of classification and strict compartmentalisation which contributed to the familiar woes of any new combat aircraft design trying to use untried technologies. Costs increased and the first flight dates came and went. When it was finally cancelled in 1991, the programme dissolved into lengthy litigation, which a decade later is still in progress. However, the process ended up revealing that inconsistent government management decisions were the main cause of the overspent budgets and delays, and that had the project proceeded, the design could have been extremely successful.

But like the B-2A, the world had moved on after the fall of the Soviet Union and another 'billion dollar' warplane, however capable, would not have survived the post-Reagan age.

Today, having been taken over by Boeing, most of the Phantom Works' projects are 'White', or as far as we know, although it retains the same approach it focused on 'Black' programmes. One of these projects was the unmanned X-36, a quarter-scale NASA/USAF technology demonstrator for an agile tailless fighter with innovative thrust-vectoring exhaust nozzles and reconfigurable controls programme.

These will demonstrate the potential of making future combat aircraft incredibly manoeuvrable while reducing weight, drag and radar cross section (RCS). The ailerons are able to raise and lower asymmetrically to provide roll control.

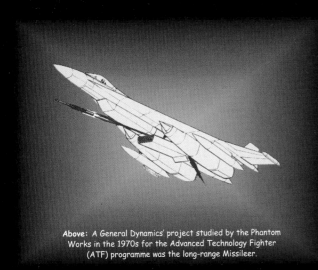

Above: A General Dynamics' project studied by the Phantom Works in the 1970s for the Advanced Technology Fighter (ATF) programme was the long-range Missileer.

The X-36 had its origins in a 1993 proposal by McDonnell Douglas to build a demonstrator for technologies to enhance tailless agile flight developed in the Phantom Works' wind tunnels since 1989. Following agreement between NASA and McDonnell Douglas to share costs in 1994, the Phantom Works designed, developed and produced the prototype X-36 in just 28 months. The total programme cost of two flyable X-36s and the flight-testing programme was only $17 million.

An important part of the X-36 programme was devoted to the development of USAF 'thinking flight control systems'. Neutral networks will allow an aircraft to survive combat damage or malfunctions by analysing and reacting to the danger in much the same

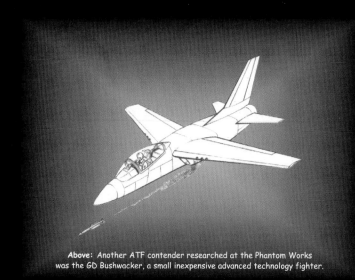

Above: Another ATF contender researched at the Phantom Works was the GD Bushwacker, a small inexpensive advanced technology fighter.

way as the human brain. The system employs software with a web of processors that learns from and adapts to its environment, rather than depending on pre-programming.

Building on its UAV technology experience, the Boeing Phantom Works is working on a Defense Advanced Research Projects Agency (DARPA)/USAF programme to develop an unmanned combat air vehicle (UCAV) for the lethal suppression of enemy air defences (SEAD) by the end of 2001. The autonomous UCAV project will use the 'thinking flight control system' developed from the X-36 programme while it will dip into the 'Black' world for stealth technology, sensor data and weapons systems.

The programme's mission is to design, build and flight test a UCAV and to demonstrate that it is capable of flying 500 miles before detecting, identifying and locating an air defence target, attacking and destroying it with live weapons, and verifying the damage. It will also have to cost less than $10 million, about a third of a CTOL JSF.

McDonnell Douglas's research into re-entry heating when designing the original Mercury space capsules was the origin of its expertise in dealing with extremes of heat and this has led to its involvement in the field of nuclear fusion research, to provide shielding. It has also led to its expertise in the area of hypersonic flight. McDonnell Douglas had proposed a Mach 12 advanced strategic reconnaissance aircraft in 1983 designed to take-off and land at conventional airfields and fly in Earth orbits more than 1,250 miles high. Since the project was related to the X-30 National Aerospace Plane (NASP) programme, part of Project *Copper Canyon*, which was cancelled in 1993, the Phantom Works has been a major participant in advancing hypersonic technology. Indeed, in 1997, a study said that a scramjet-powered B-1B-size Mach 10 aircraft, with a 5,280 mile radius of action and a 1,000lb payload, was feasible.

The Phantom Works has designed Hyper-X, a NASA programme to test scramjet propulsion technology at speeds of Mach 5 to Mach 10. The Hyper-X test vehicle, intended to be boosted to altitude on a Pegasus launch vehicle carried under the wing of NASAs NB-52, uses the same basic design as a potential Mach 10 aircraft. While originally a McDonnell Douglas design, four flight vehicles with a 5ft wingspan and

Above: The Phantom Works most famous project, the McDonnell Douglas/GD A-12 Advanced Tactical Aircraft (ATA) project for the US Navy.

Above: The X-36 is a quarter scale unmanned aerial vehicle designed to demonstrate tailless agile flight characteristics of future fighters.

ft-long are being built by Micro Craft of Tullahoma, Tennessee with a first flight planned for mid-2001. ..ain, affordability was a prime objective. The NASP cost billions and never flew. Each of the four Hyper-X ..ight vehicles is to fly once and the entire programme is planned to cost only $170 million. If the Hyper-X ..aches its design speed of Mach 7 flight, it will be the fastest-ever air-breathing winged aircraft.

. A scaled up version of the X-40A Space Manoeuvre Vehicle (SMV) is being developed at the Phantom Works for ..e USAF and the X-37 Future-X Pathfinder programme will be the first X-plane to fly in orbit to demonstrate ..e technology for a practical Reusable Launch Vehicle (RLV) that can operate in orbit, re-enter and land ..tonomously.

. Designed to reach further into space is the Solar Orbit Transfer Vehicle (SOTV), part of a USAF-sponsored ..ogramme for an autonomous spacecraft powered by thermal propulsion to demonstrate low-cost delivery of ..yloads to higher orbits.

. The Phantom Works' expertise in hypersonics is being utilised in a DARPA programme for a low-cost hypersonic ..rike missile. Intended for launch against Scud-type mobile missile launchers from aircraft and surface ships, ..e Affordable Rapid Response Missile Demonstrator (ARRMD), powered by a scramjet, will have a 400 miles stand- ..f range. Two other advanced air delivered munitions programmes, the Joint Direct Attack Munition (JDAM) and

Joint Air-to-Surface Stand-off Missile (JASSM) have recently been developed and tested at the Phantom Works. The former is now in production and was first dropped in anger by USAF B-2As on Yugoslav targets during Operation *Allied Force* while the JASSM programme with a low-cost, low-risk design was in direct competition with a formerly classified design from Lockheed's Skunk Works known as the Wind Corrected Munitions Dispenser (WCMD).

Another programme has been Boeing's concept for a Small Smart Bomb. This is a stealthy 250 lb weapon intended for internal carriage by JSF and other low-observable aircraft. Although it would only have some 50 lb of high-technology composition explosive, that meets new requirements for insensitive munitions, it will be able to penetrate 6 ft of concrete with an extreme accuracy by using multiple guidance technologies including an INS, jam-proof GPS, and LIDAR.

On a more mundane level, its Common Operational Flight Program (COFP) aims to improve vital software used today by all state-of-the-art combat aircraft by improving its reusability and increasing its ability to run on commercial-off-the-shelf (COTS) computers. This software, which cuts the costs of design and maintenance, was flight tested in 1996 on F/A-18Cs and AV-8Bs, and has applicability to future design programmes, such as that of the Joint Strike Fighter (JSF).

The High Stability Engine Control (HSEC) Program saw the Phantom Works joining with NASA, the USAF, and Pratt & Whitney to develop and test an advanced engine control system on a modified F-15 that will potentially prevent compressor stalls and engine failures by using a high-speed computerised sensor with appropriate software to respond to high levels of engine inlet airflow turbulence or distortion, which could increase the manoeuvrability of future fighter aircraft.

Other major Phantom Works' programmes include the Canard Rotor Wing (CRW) *Dragonfly*, the Blended Wing Body (BWB) No-Tail Advanced Tactical Transport (NOTAIL ATT) and the DARPA Unmanned Combat Air Vehicle (UCAV) to demonstrate the feasibility of using unmanned strike aircraft using X-36 technology. Using technology developed under President Reagan's 'Star Wars' Strategic Defense Initiative in the late 1980s, Boeing has flown the prototype YAL-1 Airborne Laser missile defence aircraft which has the Phantom Works studying the application of diode-pumped solid-state lasers. Each USAF AL-1 aircraft, based on the Boeing 747 airframe, will cost some $800 million while a shot from the high-energy laser missile will be less than $60,000.

Although the Phantom Works has successfully adapted to the 'new world order', many of its diverse products will continue to have a military bias which would suggest that should there ever be a requirement for a 'Black' programme in the future, it will be well placed to host it.

The current direction of the Phantom Works shows how it has adapted to the end of the Cold War.

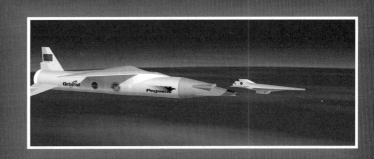

Above: The air-launched scramjet-powered Mach 7.0 Hyper-X test vehicle designed at the Phantom Works is about to begin flight trials.

Up and Away

Up and Away

Right: One of Germany's most incredible Emergency Fighter Programme (EFP) projects was the Focke-Wulf *Triebflugal*, a coleocopter point-defence interceptor.

The ability to operate an aircraft from battle-damaged runways was yet another characteristic that war planners have wrestled with since the aircraft first went to war. In the dying months of World War Two, with Allied bombers carrying out round-the-clock heavy bombing raids on *Luftwaffe* airfields, desperate measures were called for.

One of these was a manned version of the Fiesler Fi-103 V-1 'Doodlebug', Germany's remote piloted flying bomb. Launched from short rail ramps, the pulse jet-powered *Reichenberg* R-IV was designed as an expendable ground attack aircraft. It had a maximum speed of over 400 mph, and could carry its 2,000 lb warhead over a maximum range of 200 miles. Planned to be operated by the *Leonidas Staffel* of the *Luftwaffe's* secret 'Special Forces' group, KG200, its pilots were to aim the R-IV at a high value target before ejecting.

A second project was Bachem Ba 349 *Natter* (Viper), a rocket-powered interceptor secretly sponsored by Heinrich Himmler's SS. Built mainly of wood, the *Natter* would be vertically launched from temporary ramps and climb to attack Allied bombers with a battery of 24 73 mm *Flohn* rockets at over 500 mph. Its endurance was only two minutes and after the fuel was exhausted, the rocket compartment would separate from the cockpit and both would parachute to earth.

The most radical vertical take-off project to almost see the light of day was the Focke-Wulf *Triebflugel*. This was a coleocopter point-defence interceptor powered by three 'steerable' Pabst ramjets mounted at the tip of three wing blades. It also required three Walter auxiliary rockets to assist its vertical take-off. Armed with two 30 mm and two 20 mm cannon, an estimated speed of over 600 mph and a maximum range of 1,500 miles, it would have been a formidable, if unlikely, adversary.

Both the *Reichenberg* and *Natter* were extensively flight-tested and put into production as part of Germany's 1944 Emergency Fighter Programme, but thankfully for the Allies, they were too few, too late.

Above: Another German vertical take-off interceptor was the rocket-powered Bacham Ba 349 *Natter* which actually went into production in 1945.

The concept of a vertical take-off combat aircraft had been recognised but it would not be until the late 1950s that a spate of advanced experimental vertical take-off and landing aircraft (VTOL) made an appearance. Designed as a shipborne fighter, the Convair XFY-1 *Pogo* was powered by a powerful turboprop engine driving two contra-rotating propellers. Standing on four wheels attached to the tips of its delta wings, tail fin and jettisonable ventral fin, the pilot had to climb a 20 ft ladder to reach the cockpit. Another 'tail-stander' was the jet-powered Ryan X-13 *VertiJet* while the British Short SC1 VTOL aircraft developed from the Rolls-Royce 'Flying Bedstead', was not a 'tail-

Above: US soldiers inspect the cockpit of a captured manned version of the V-1 'Doodlebug' flying bomb known as the *Reichenberg* R-IV.

stander'. A small delta-wing aircraft standing on a conventional tri-cycle landing gear, the SC1 achieved vertical take-off by using four downward-pointing Rolls-Royce RB.018 turbofans while forward speed and conventional landing came from the thrust of a fifth engine in the tail.

Potentially the most advanced VTOL programs of the 1950s was the ultra secret Canadian Project 'Y' fighter which lay under wraps for half a century. The Avro-Canada programme called for the design and flight test of a technology demonstrator for a 'tail-stander' Mach 3.0 fighter aircraft that could take-off and land vertically.

The flying-wing design was intended to be powered by revolutionary radical-flow jets with exhaust gases emitting from dozens of small angled nozzles in the wing's leading edges. Because of its flying-wing configuration and serrated leading edges, Project 'Y' would have been the first truly 'stealthy' supersonic fighter. However, the Canadian government could not afford the rising development costs and in 1954 the USAF took over the technology data, but by 1961 the project was killed. Or was it?

Above: The Hawker Kestrel, which became the world's first operational VTOL fighter when it joined a tri-national evaluation squadron in 1965, is seen here carrying rocket pods.

Above: Development of the Kestrel/Harrier family of VTOL combat aircraft was taken over by McDonnell Douglas which produced the Harrier II operated by the RAF as the Harrier GR.7.

In the event, the first successful VTOL combat aircraft would use none of these heavy and cumbersome methods to attain vertical take-off and fast forward speed combined with the ability to carry a reasonable weapons load. The breakthrough came following the American Mutual Weapons Development Program (MWDP) Agency's interest in VTOL aircraft for military operations in the mid-fifties, and a French engineer's experiments with vectoring thrust jet engines.

Michel Wibault joined Bristol Aero Engines after no interest was shown in his concepts in his native France. The result of his work was the vectored thrust Bristol Pegasus which was partly funded by the MWDP and would power Hawker's new VTOL project P.1127 which started as a private venture with no British government funding, or even requirement.

Work began in great secrecy in 1958 and in less than two years the P.1127 made its first tethered vertical flight. When it was revealed to the general public at the 1962 Farnborough Show, its performance was greeted by something bordering on disbelief - the dream fantasy of VTOL seemed to have come true.

A tri-national evaluation squadron was formed with Britain, Germany and the United States in 1964 with nine Hawker *Kestrel* F(GA).1s, a militarised derivative of the P.1127 and six *Kestrels* were subsequently transferred to the USA in 1965 for evaluation by the USMarine Corps.

Above: *A two-seat Harrier T.4 is being used by the UK's Defence Research Agency (DRA) for STOVL trials for the Joint Strike Fighter (JSF) programme.*

The *Kestrel* was largely a subsonic technology demonstrator for a supersonic derivative, the P.1154 which was cancelled by the British Labour government in its 1964 defence economy drive. However, the RAF was able to order more than 100 subsonic single-seat close support and reconnaissance developments of the *Kestrel*, known as the *Harrier*, which entered service in 1970. A similar number was later ordered by the USMC, designated the AV-8A, and the Royal Navy acquired a multi-role variant following the retirement of the service's large conventional aircraft carriers in 1977. These fought with distinction in the South Atlantic during the 1982 Anglo-Argentine Falkland Islands conflict. In the subsequent three-month Operation *Corporate*, 28 *Sea Harriers* flew 1,450 missions downing more than 20 Argentine aircraft for the loss of five, none in air combat. Fourteen RAF *Harriers* flew 126 ground attack missions using 'smart' bombs for the first time, with three being lost to ground fire.

This conflict had proved to the world what British forces had known all along, that without the operationally flexible, rugged *Harrier* and *Sea Harrier* with their unique ability to operate from short strips, roads, helipads and ships, the Falkland Islands, 8,000 miles away from the UK, could not have been retaken. Despite its operational success the *Harrier* design was already more than 20 years old and required a radical redesign to enable it to maintain its advantage over some conventional attack aircraft. However, the British government showed no further interest in advancing the design and McDonnell Douglas acquired the production and development rights to the *Harrier*.

Above: US Advanced Technology Fighter (ATF) contender, GD's *Jiminy Cricket* was designed to use multiple jet engines for short or vertical take-offs and landings.

An improved *Harrier II*, with a completely new composite wing and upgraded Roll-Royce Pegasus, was ordered by the USMC, designated AV-8B, the RAF, and Italian and Spanish navies. Although it had a proven combat record in both the Gulf War and Balkans conflicts, the *Harrier II* was still subsonic and the search for a supersonic VSTOL fighter persisted. McDonnell Douglas itself had produced a number of *Super Harrier* concepts including its Model 279-3, but for one reason or the other, none were developed.

Grumman entered the VTOL arena in the mid-1970s with a radical ship-borne strike/reconnaissance concept. The single-seat '*Nutcracker*' featured a hinged rear fuselage carrying two turbofans, that would hinge downwards for hovering or vertical flight. Launching and recovery to small ships involved the aircraft engaging a drogue-tipped crane in a similar way to an airship's mooring mast. The '*Nutcracker*' was then lowered onto the ship's helipad. It was never built!

One of the reasons why supersonic VTOL aircraft took so long to become a practical reality was that the advanced engines of the stillborn P.1154, and the later BAe P.1214-3, a forward-swept wing (FSW) supersonic VSTOL project, would have used burned fuel in the fan nozzles to give them a Mach 2 capability but this would have produced super-heated exhaust emissions that would potentially damage any landing pad in the ground hover mode. Some of these problems were addressed in different ways when designs incorporating short take-off and landing (STOL), short take-off and vertical landing (STOVL) and vertical take-off and landing (VTOL) were evaluated in early USAF Advanced Tactical Fighter (ATF) studies of the 1970s and 1980s. The benefits of abbreviated take-offs and landings were, however, less clear than benefits associated with stealth, speed and manoeuvrability.

Above: Lockheed Martin's X-35A is the conventional take-off and landing (CTOL) contender for the US tri-service Joint Strike Fighter (JSF) competition.

'*Short Snort*' and '*Jiminy Cricket*' were two General Dynamics (GD) designs that addressed STOL more directly. '*Short Snort*' vectored thrust from the engine over the wing to produce a fighter with runway requirements of only a few hundred feet. The concept employed ducts and ports that diverted engine exhaust out span-wise along the top of the wing. The approach generated tremendous amounts of lift at very low speeds. However, the ducting was very heavy and ultimately proved impossible to incorporate in a high-performance supersonic fighter.

'*Jiminy Cricket*' attacked the STOL problem with multiple engines pioneered by the British Short SC.1 of the 1950s. The design had a main lift-cruise engine that provided thrust for lift and for forward flight, and auxiliary engines mounted vertically that provided lift for take-offs and landing only, giving it either a STOL or VTOL capability depending on the size of the engines.

A fighter designed for supersonic flight and high manoeuvrability has a thrust-to-weight ratio and wing loading that produce a fair amount of inherent short airfield performance which can be improved with the addition of

Above: Two decades before JSF, the GD *Short Snort* ATF STOL concept used vectored engine thrust over the wings to increase lift.

Below: The ASTOVL version of Lockheed Martin's X-35 JSF employs a novel lift-fan system with a three-piece rotating asymmetric exhaust duct segment designed by Rolls-Royce to provide additional lift.

rough-field landing gear, oversize brakes and thrust reversers. The weight of these improvements, however, decreases the thrust-to-weight ratio available in air combat.

ATF originally had a very difficult STOL requirement that called for the use of some of these features, most notably thrust reversing and thrust vectoring. The take-off and landing distances were relaxed during the demonstration/validation phase of the programme to eliminate the need for reversers as well as their extra weight and cost. Thrust vectoring was retained since it improves aircraft performance in several ways. Thrust vectoring can be used to shorten take-offs by rotating the nose of an aircraft up at a lower speed than would be possible by using tail surfaces alone.

In cruise, vectoring can be used to supplement the trim normally provided by tail surfaces. Vectoring therefore allows smaller tails or allows cruise with tails set to a position that produces less drag. Thrust vectoring can also augment control power at high angles of attack or during aggressive manoeuvres.

Neither of these concepts were adopted in the final ATF design which resulted in the YF-22 and YF-23, but an even larger US multi-role fighter programme, the Joint Strike Fighter (JSF), has a major short take-off and vertical landing (STOVL) requirement for both the USMC and Royal Navy variants.

The STOVL version is the most complex, and potentially most expensive of the JSF family and there are growing doubts about the advantage that it offers over conventional take-off and landing (CTOL) being developed for the US Air Force and Navy. Since the Gulf War ended, USMC AV-8Bs have not taken part in any other live operation although small numbers of RAF Harriers flying from large fixed air bases in NATO countries and carrier-borne RN SHARs have been in subsequent actions over the former Yugoslavia. Some defence planners have argued that the *Harrier*'s original mission, of close support from makeshift Forward Operating Bases (FOB) for ground forces as they make rapid advances on the set-piece battlefield, is now redundant in current and projected limited war scenarios.

Nevertheless, more than 25% of the JSF programme will be devoted to a STOVL version which will inevitably be a compromise between providing additional power for vertical lift

Above: Planview of the Lockheed Martin F-35B ASTOVL JSF.

Below: Boeing's ASTOVL X-32B concept of the JSF is designed to be a multi-role replacement for the US Marine Corps' AV-8B Harrier IIs.

and a reduced combat radius and weapon load. Two
JSF STOVL concept demonstrators, Boeing's X-32B
and Lockheed Martin's X-36B, are about to make
their first flights and a winner will be declared
in 2003.

The system adopted for Boeing's ASTOVL X-32B is
a three-segment Harrier-style direct-lift
arrangement with engine exhaust ducted forwards to
two rotating direct lift nozzles via vortex flaps
under the centre point of the fuselage. A front
nozzle is fed by bleed air via a jet screen duct
with an anti-recirculation shield which is
extended aft of the nose wheel bay. Additional
control in the vertical landing mode is provided
by bleed air fed to wingtip roll-control nozzles
via ducting along the wing trailing edges, and yaw
nozzles located each side of the two-dimensional,
pitch-vectoring propulsion nozzle.

To improve airflow to the engine at low speed
to zero, a translating chin inlet cowl moves
forward when the aircraft transitions from forward
flight to the hover. Although it will not have to
power a separate direct lift fan, the engine used
by Boeing's ASTOVL JSF will have to be at a higher
power rating than that of its competitors due to
it providing all the lift through the three
nozzles and will therefore use more fuel in the
hover. However, in conventional flight mode it
will never have to use full power, thus saving
engine life and improving fuel consumption.

Lockheed Martin's JSF concept resembles a
scaled-down F-22 airframe with the ATOVL X-36B
powered by a lift-fan system developed in the
Skunk Works. The Allison-built direct lift fan,
located behind the cockpit, is powered by a shaft
drive from the main F119 after-burning turbofan
derivative with additional lift provided by a
stealthy three-piece rotating asymmetric exhaust
duct segment designed by Rolls-Royce which was
inspired by the innovative Soviet Yak-141
Freestyle.

Above: A USMC Lockheed Martin F-35B JSF hover-lands on to
the flight deck of a Marine Corps assault carrier.

Above: US Navy CTOL versions of JSF, the
Lockheed Martin F-32A are launched from the
forward 'cats' of a conventional carrier.

The Soviet Union was the only other country to produce a successful STOVL attack aircraft to rival the *Harrier*. Designed by the Yakovlev Design Bureau, which had already built a series of experimental STOVL prototypes in the 1960s, the multi-role Yak-38 made its operational debut with the Soviet Naval Aviation in the mid-1970s. Although similar in size to the *Harrier*, it had a Short SC.1-style direct lift system comprising two vertical RD-38 turbojets mounted in tandem behind the cockpit, and a main cruise engine with limited thrust vectoring nozzles.

Above: A Lockheed Martin ASTOVL F-35B shown in Royal Navy colours.

Above: A British option for the Royal Navy's Advanced Carrier Borne Aircraft (FCBA) is the Super Harrier Mk.3 as seen in this AVPRO concept.

Above: Russia's Yakovlev Design Bureau successful STOVL designs include the Yak-38, left, and Yak-141.

Due to the extremely high fuel consumption during STOVL operations, this arrangement severely limited its range and stores payload. The subsonic Yak-38's combat radius was less than 250 miles (400 km) and although this could be increased by carrying external fuel tanks on two of its four underwing hardpoints, its armament was then restricted to only two AA-2 *Atoll* IR AAMs.

Despite its shortcomings, the Yak-38, code-named *Forger*, gave the Soviet Navy valuable experience of operating a

35

jet STOVL type. Some 200 were built and operated in air groups aboard four Soviet *Kiev*-class cruiser carriers with the Northern and Pacific Fleets for over a decade. It carried a number of advanced on-board systems such as full weapons system and a take-off control system which during a short roll automatically transitioned the aircraft into vertical take-off. Approach and vertical landing on a flight deck was automatically guided by laser as soon as the *Forger* captured the carrier's ILS.

Above: The Yak-38 *Forger* was operated by the Soviet Navy as a shipboard strike fighter for more than two decades.

All Yak-38s were fitted with the extremely efficient K-36LV seat which automatically triggered the ejection sequence once the combination of vertical speed, height and speed became out of limits. Of more than 30 pilots that ejected using this system, only one was killed.

Valuable lessons learned from the Yak-38 programme were fed into its successor, the Yak-141, the world's first supersonic STOVL fighter which was optimised for the air defence role with a secondary attack capability. Adopting a similar layout to its predecessor of twin lift engines plus a main engine, the Yak-141 differed by having a single rotating after-burning nozzle slightly behind its centre of gravity.

Above: The world's first supersonic STOVL fighter was the Yak-141 *Freestyle* seen here in the hover mode with lift engine inlet open and hinged jet-pipe pointing downwards.

A slab tailplane and twin canted fins were therefore mounted on deep booms, the inner walls of which were made of titanium while the airframe was constructed mainly of aluminium-lithium alloy and composite materials. The underside of the fuselage, which had to withstand tremendous heat from the exhaust gases of the 34,000 lb thrust R-79 turbofan and twin 9,400 lb thrust RD-41 lift engines during vertical take-off and landing, was coated with heat-resistant resin putty.

Two prototype *Freestyles* were constructed in the late-1980s fitted with Yak-38M Phase II avionics and digital Fly-by-Wire (FBW) flight/engine controls linked to its flight control computer to give all-weather manual or

Above: One of two Yak-141 prototypes that was used for a number of successful flight deck landings on the Soviet carrier *Tbilisi*, later the Admiral *Kutznetsov*.

Above: Following an engine fire, the Yak-141 was severely damaged in 1991 after crashing on Tbilisi's flight deck. Test pilot Vladimir Yakimov ejected without injury.

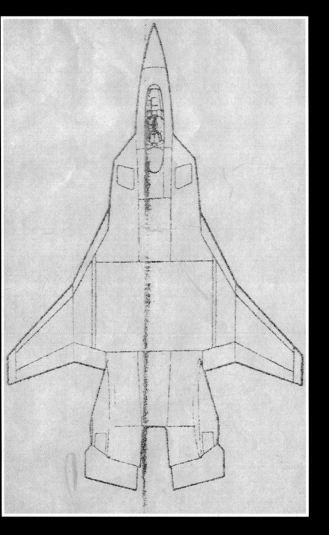

automatic take-offs and landings. The projected production version was designed to carry a 9,000 lb weapon load with a combat radius of 550 miles.

After more than 150 hours of successful flight trials, the programme was terminated by two unrelated events. Firstly, following the disintegration of the Soviet Union, the new Russian Navy terminated further funding in September 1991, a few weeks before one of the prototypes was badly damaged during carrier landing trials when it caught fire following a heavy landing due to partial engine failure.

Although the Yakovlev Bureau managed to continue flight testing its surviving Yak-141, which was only a technology for the more advanced Yak-201, for another year, the development programme was cancelled at the end of 1992.   However the following year, Lockheed Martin awarded the Yakovlev Design Bureau a $500,000 contract for assisting with the design of the rotating main jet nozzle for its ASTOVL JSF version and Pratt & Whitney had a similar agreement with the Russian Soyuz Aero-Engine company.

While the dream of a successful STOVL fighter seems to be becoming a reality in the confines of Lockheed Martin's Skunk works and Boeing's Phantom Works, its recent operations, such as *Desert Fox* and *Allied Force*, have highlighted the fact that there may only be a limited requirement for VSTOL

Above, right and opposite page: The supersonic multi-role Yak-201 was a projected production version of the Yak-141 *Freestyle* for the Soviet Navy but when development funding was terminated in 1991, some of its lift-engine technology was acquired by Lockheed Martin JSF team for $1/2million.

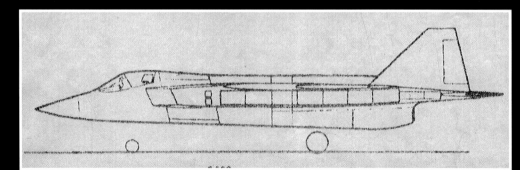

Harrier-type aircraft in the future. With the benefit of air refuelling, and air superiority having been achieved early in the operations, conventional take-off and landing (CTOL) attack aircraft can reach their targets carrying a heavier weapon payload than current VSTOL aircraft. Their main role of providing Close Air Support (CAS) for ground forces from Forward Operating Bases (FOB) over a rapidly moving battlefield is seen as less and less relevant to future limited war and peacekeeping scenarios.

Above: The forward-swept wing ASTOVL BAe P.1214-3 concept was a supersonic Harrier replacement proposal.

Incorporating a short or vertical take-off and landing capability comes at a high price. Establishing the need for the capability is very complex. How much of this capability is needed depends on the size and effectiveness of an enemy's offensive counter-air and runway-busting weapons. It also depends on the number of runways that an enemy needs to wreck to significantly affect the other side's ability to fly and on its ability to quickly repair runways and get back into operation. Most importantly, it depends on the effectiveness of defending air forces in stopping enemy sorties from reaching a base in the first place.

Whether to bomb concrete or bomb aircraft on the ground further complicates the issue. The effectiveness of aircraft shelters and the accuracy of intelligence about where aircraft are at any given time play a role in the latter approach. During the Cold War the United States and its NATO allies were busy developing a variety of air-to-ground weapons for busting large expanses of concrete and it could be reasonably assumed that the Warsaw Pact would reply in kind.

All of this begs the question, is an ASTOVL version of JSF, the most complex and expensive of the three types, still a military reality?

Force Multipliers

Above: Russia's Mil Mi-26 *Halo* is the world's largest operational helicopter with a 105ft diameter rotor.

For the past 40 years, the most prolific heavy-lift helicopter has been the ubiquitous twin-engine CH-47 *Chinook*. Having first flown in 1959 to meet the US Army's requirement for a turbine-engined all-weather cargo helicopter, by 1972, more than 500 had served in Vietnam carrying everything from M198 155 mm howitzers to refugees, no less than 147 of them and their belongings on one occasion. It remained in the frontline of numerous conflicts including the Falklands, Gulf War, and the Balkans, not only in the medium lift role but also as an Electronic Warfare (EW) platform and dedicated long-range Special Forces helicopter.

Its only rival for operational longevity is the C-130 *Hercules* while the only rotary-wing aircraft that can outperform it in the power and weight stakes are the US Marine's three-engined Sikorsky CH-53 *Super Stallion* and Russia's Mi-26 *Halo*, the largest helicopter in the world. Although still in production at the beginning of the 21st century, the *Chinook*'s days are numbered by the US military's Future Transport Rotorcraft (FTR) programme which is aiming for an in-service date of 2020.

Several new vertical heavy-lift concepts are being evaluated for a *Chinook* replacement, with the tilt-rotor being among the front runners. If there is an aircraft concept that has fought hard for its place in aviation history, it is the tilt-rotor, a hybrid design that is a cross between a helicopter and a conventional aircraft that offers both military and civilian customers unparalleled operational flexibility and versatility.

It is not a new concept yet it is only in the 21st century that it getting the full recognition it deserves. In 1951 Bell started the first serious research in the tilt-rotor concept with the XV-3, which was followed by the Vertol VZ-2 in 1956. Many other companies were to experiment with tilt-rotors and tilt-fans during this period, which clearly indicated the advantage of combining the speed of a conventional aircraft, with the flexibility of the helicopter's vertical take-off and landing capability. The range of these craft was also superior to the helicopter, and it was clear that they had a future with the military for a variety of operational roles.

Above: Bell Boeing's V-22 Osprey tilt-rotor in transition to hover mode.

In fact the concept had been researched a decade earlier by German aeronautical engineers during the desperate dying days of the Third Reich. Helicopter pioneers Heinrich Focke and Gerd Achgelis formed a company in 1937 to develop their rotary wing concepts. After producing a rudimentary one-man towed autogyro, the *Bachstelze* (Wagtail) and the advanced twin-rotor Fa 223 *Drache* (Dragon), one of which flew across the English Channel at the end of the war, they began to explore a tilt-rotor project.

The Focke-Achgelis Fa 269 programme began in 1941 and resembled a conventional aircraft that was able to take-off and land vertically be means of swivelling propellers mounted in each wing. These would swivel under the wing to the vertical position to provide lift, then turn to the rear to drive the aircraft forward at an estimated 375 mph. The problem was that it required an extremely long and unwieldy landing gear to give clearance to the propellers when the aircraft was on the ground and the programme could be counted as a near miss.

Above: The V-22 Osprey flying in forward cruise mode driven by large diameter propellers.

Above: The turbo-prop powered Bell Boeing V-22 Osprey is the first operational tilt-rotor since Bell began development of the concept 50 years ago.

It was in 1973 that Bell demonstrated a proof of concept tilt-rotor known as the XV-15. This programme proved to be highly successful, and ended with Bell and Boeing-Vertol joining forces to build a scaled up version of XV-15 to be known as the V-22 *Osprey*. Developed for the Joint Services Advanced Vertical Lift Aircraft (JSAVLA) programme, formally known as JVX, the V-22 combines the vertical lift capability of the helicopter with the fast-cruise performance of a fixed-wing turboprop aircraft.

The aircraft, powered by two 6,150 shp Allison T406-AD-400 engines, has an interconnecting transmission shaft that provides a means of equal power in the event of an engine failure. After taking off vertically the nacelles rotate 90 degrees forward, converting the aircraft into a conventional turboprop airplane. It can carry 24 troops or the same weight in cargo at speeds up to 300 knots in all weathers, day or night, and can be refuelled in mid-air.

Prime customers for the *Osprey* are American at present, although the UK is currently evaluating the tilt-rotor for an Airborne Early Warning (AEW) role or for troop carrying missions. The V-22 features a novel automatic rotor folding system, that allows for stowage aboard ships and heavy-lift transport aircraft, making it very easy to move over long distances to overseas theatres.

Above: Boeing's proposed SSTOL No-tail Advanced Theatre Transport (NOTAIL ATT), the tilt-wing Super Frog.

Even at this stage of its development the V-22 Osprey has been under threat on several occasions. In 1992 the US Secretary for Defense tried to cancel the programme but Congress blocked this move. A series of fatal accidents also caused problems, but again these setbacks were overcome and the project is now far more secure.

The USMC recently stated that *Osprey* was its number one priority that will give it a massive increase in operational capability for out-of-area (OOA) operations. The USMC *Osprey*, designated MV-22, will be used for amphibious assaults from carriers and land bases, carrying troops, equipment and supplies to forward operating bases (FOB).

Designated HV-22, the US Navy will use its *Osprey* variant for CSAR, logistical support and for the insertion and extraction of Special Forces. The USAF will operate their aircraft, the CV-22, in much the same way as the Navy while the Army's MV-22 will be used for aero-medical evacuation, Special Operations, logistic support and combat air assaults. In the latter role, weapons such as mini-guns and lightweight cannon will be fitted for self-protection.

Other developments could include an *Osprey* gunship to take the place of the *Cobra* attack helicopter which will not be able to keep up with the V-22.

The concept of tilt-rotors has clearly now been proved, and a future heavy lift aircraft is planned, featuring four engines with a cargo carrying capability equivalent to a C-130 *Hercules*. Known as Quad Tilt Rotor (QTR), this aircraft has been proposed by Bell-Boeing for the USAF heavy tactical airlift requirement which is part of the JTR programme, and will clearly provide a more flexible approach then a conventional transport aircraft.

The US Army requires an aircraft to carry a payload of between 10-20 tonne over a range of 650 miles. Larger prop-rotor diameters combined with advanced blade technologies will make the QTR more efficient and give it a better performance than conventional transports. Blades filled with 'smart' shape-memory alloys (SMA) and ceramic materials developed at the Massachusetts Institute of Technology (MIT) can twist themselves to alter airflow controlling the aircraft's pitch. The shape changing blades reduce weight and increase reliability.

Boeing is also proposing yet another adaptation of the tilt-rotor which owes its genesis more to the Canadair CL-84 and Hiller Ryan XC-142 tilt-wings of the 1960s. These had only limited rotation of the propellers to give a super-short take-off and landing (SSTOL) rather than the full vertical take-off and landing (VTOL) capability of the QTR.

The projected Boeing No-tail Advanced Theatre Transport (NOTAIL ATT) known as *Super Frog*, is being designed at the Phantom Works to carry a 30 tonne payload, over a 2,000 mile range. Powered by four 12,000 shp-class advanced turboprops inter-linked with lightweight cross-shafts for added redundancy, the ATT will be required to operate from a 1,000 ft airstrip and land and take-off fully loaded at only 40 knots.

With Boeing having a foot in both the QTR and ATT camps, it will be in a good position to challenge Lockheed's 50-year stranglehold in the medium-range tactical transport sector, with the C-130. However, it may face a challenge from Europe with the stealthy X-wing *Titan*.

The *Titan* has been designed to be capable of meeting the US requirement for a new heavy lift VTOL vehicle with a maximum payload of 60 tonnes and able to carry two Armoured Personnel Carriers (APC). For self-protection it could be armed with forward and rearward cannon turrets plus AIM-9 or AIM-120 air-to-air missiles.

Below: The stealthy X-wing Titan is an innovative concept from the UK company AVPRO designed as a Chinook replacement.

To improve the combat effectiveness of the vehicle, its operational range can be extended by air refuelling (AR) while the aircraft is operating in conventional mode with the X-wing stationary during which it would be capable of a cruise speed in excess of 300 mph.

An innovative gas-driven X-wing rotor would provide VTOL lift in the same way as a conventional helicopter rotor but is driven by high-pressure air bled from the twin turbofan engines. The air exits the blades through nozzles located at the blade tips causing them to rotate. In order to provide a large payload capability, especially in VTOL mode, combined with high speed cruise, advanced composite materials would be used for the primary structure wherever possible. These give significant advantages over metals, such as low weight, high strength, improved fatigue resistance, damage tolerance and negligible corrosion.

Above: A Russian design for a SSTOL tactical transport from the Myasishchyev Design Bureau features both swing-wing and X-wing.

Powered by two high bypass ratio turbofans, the *Titan*'s large rotor diameter, some 125 ft, results in improved propulsive efficiency thereby consuming less fuel in VTOL mode than a craft with smaller diameter rotors, which leads to improved range and endurance.

In VTOL flight, the exhaust efflux is deflected downward and over the sides of the aircraft, which acts as infra-red (IR) suppressers to reduce the threat from IR-homing missiles. The leading edges of the rotors contain multi-element phased array radar with electronic beam steering. This provides the crew with 360° radar coverage while the X-wing is rotating and when stationary, as each blade can cover a 90° scan zone.

Data obtained from the radar could be data-linked from the vehicle to AWACS or JSTARS aircraft, or direct to other friendly forces. In essence, the aircraft is capable of performing reconnaissance, SIGINT or ELINT operations in addition to carrying out its transport mission, a true force multiplier.

The X-wing concept was taken to its extreme by a Russian design of similar size and payload to the *Titan*. Designed by idiosyncratic Myasishchyev design bureau, the CMC was a unique swing-wing/X-wing concept using the fuselage based on the bureau's MM-1 twin-turboprop transport. Powered by two turbofans for forward cruise, power could be bled off to drive its X-wing rotor when the main wings were moved forward for a short landing.

After an equally short take-off from 1,000 ft unmade airstrips, the CMC would accelerate to 150 mph when the X-wing would fold back and the main wings move to full sweep-back to reach its a cruising speed of 300 mph. This complex craft has yet to receive government funding.

Above: The world's first military airlifter was the Messerschmitt Me 323 *Gigant* (Giant) that first flew in late 1941.

Prompted by the lack of the Coalition's heavy lift capabilities during the Gulf War, particularly when speed of reaction was vital in the *Desert Shield* build up phase, and the European NATO members' shortfall in any type of strategic transport assets, new solutions are under serious consideration at the start of the 21st century.

In the short term, there are only two contenders for the European Staff Requirement (ESR) for a future military airlifter, the Boeing C-17A *Globemaster III*, which is in USAF service with three being leased to the RAF, and the Ukrainian An-70. The concept of a large airlifter aircraft can again be traced back to World War Two and to Germany in particular.

In 1943, the six-engine Messerschmitt Me 323 *Gigant* (Giant) went into service with the *Luftwaffe* in North Africa. Developed from the 180 ft wingspan Me 321 heavy transport glider, the *Gigant* featured clam-shell doors in the nose for easy loading of vehicles and bulky cargo, and could accommodate up to 200 fully equipped troops (standing), or 60 stretchers and medical attendants. Its maximum payload was a staggering 16 tonnes

Above: Developed from a giant glider, the Me 323 *Gigant* was one of the largest aircraft of World War Two.

Above: The Airbus A400M is a contender for the European Staff Requirement (ESR) for a future NATO military airlifter.

which was not matched by any Allied aircraft until the appearance of the original Douglas *Globemaster* of the 1950s.

Some 60 years later, the European aerospace consortium, Airbus, which includes Germany's DaimlerChrysler company, entered the heavy-lift arena with two contenders for the ESR and the UK RAF requirement for a Future Transport Aircraft (FTA). The Airbus A400M is a projected tactical transport powered by four advanced turboprop engines to carry a payload of 30 tonnes up to 3,000 miles. Featuring a two-crew glass cockpit, one or more loadmasters will be accommodated in an independent workstation to operate, load and unload the pressurised cargo deck.

Above: To be used in either the long-range transport or strategic tanker roles, 25 Airbus A400Ms have been ordered by the RAF.

A second Airbus contender is a development of the A300-608ST Beluga Super Transporter, designed for transporting large Airbus sub-assemblies, including wings which are loaded through a hinged nose section above the cockpit, between manufacturing sites in the UK, Germany, Spain and France.

The outsiders for the European competition are two Ukrainian Antonovs. A consortium of German aerospace companies continues to back a NATO spec development of the An-70, known as the An-7X or Medium Transport Aircraft (MTA). Unlike the A400M, the An-70, which first flew in 1994, has a payload of 50 tonnes, is powered by four propfans and is due to enter service with the Russian Air Force in 2004.

Its larger brother, the heavyweight An-124 *Ruslan*, is the world's largest operational aircraft with a wingspan of 240 ft, a payload of 150 tonnes and has been offered to the RAF fitted with four Rolls-Royce RB211 turbofans. Another East European airlifter which has yet to take to the air is the Russian Tu-330, a twin-turbofan tactical transport designed to carry a 35 tonne payload.

Above: Designed to carry twice the payload of a C-130 faster and further, A400M production will be shared by six European countries.

Right: A UK proposal for and ultra super-short take off and landing (SSTOL) jet-powered advanced theater transport.

Even larger than the An-124 is the giant Russian Myasishchyev M-90 Multipurpose Cargo Aircraft (MCA). Powered by eight turboprop engines and with a wingspan of over 300 ft, the M-90 was designed to carry payloads of up to 400 tonnes in a large 200 ft-long removable cylindrical container slung under the main wing between two boons which carried the aircrew, fuel and the 52-wheel landing gear. The concept bore a close resemblance to the World War Two German Daimler-Benz 'A', a projected long-range bomber combination that carried a small jet attack aircraft in the same way as the M-90 would carry its cargo container.

With the end of the long C-130 line in view, Lockheed Martin has expressed an interest in joining the European airlifter project which could also be a contender for the USAF's C-141 *Starlifter* replacement, although the US company has already come up with some radical and innovative proposals of its own. The most interesting of these is the Joint-Wing tanker/transport concept which has no vertical tail, but a slim swept-back wing joining an equally slim and long swept-forward tailplane. The aircraft resembles a futuristic 'biplane' with the upper FSW tailplane joined to the lower swept-back mainplane by vertical wingtip struts. The biplane configuration gives added lift for extra payload and short take-off, high-speed cruise and excellent low-speed handling.

With so many players in 'trash-hauling' sector, there is all to play for on the future heavy-lifter front.

Left: A Ukranian contender for the ESR came in the shape of the Antonov An-70 which can carry a payload of 50 tonnes.

Right: The An-70's distinctive multi-paddle bladed airscrews give the propfan-powered airlifter an excellent short-field performance.

UR-NTK

Above: The Boeing C-17A Globemaster III entered USAF service in 1993 and has played a major role in recent Balkans operations.

Below: Four C-17A will be leased from Boeing in 2002 for a short-term enhancement of the RAF's airlift capability

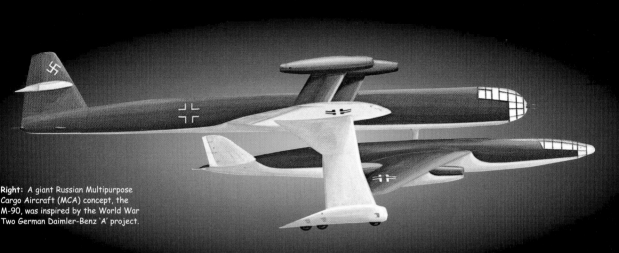

Right: A giant Russian Multipurpose Cargo Aircraft (MCA) concept, the M-90, was inspired by the World War Two German Daimler-Benz 'A' project.

Below: A proposed replacement for USAF's C-141 Starlifter is Lockheed Martin's innovative Joint-Wing tanker/transport.

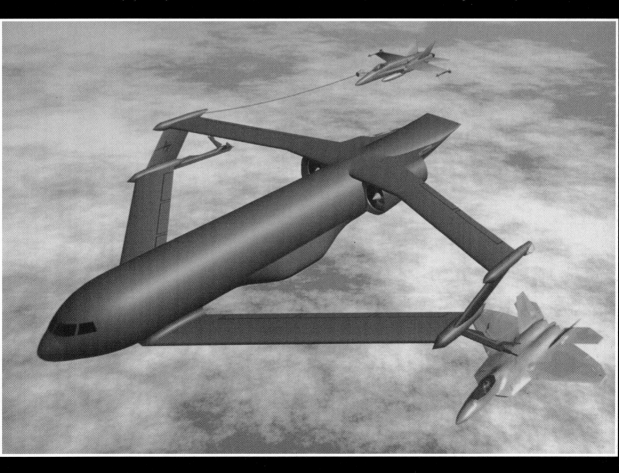

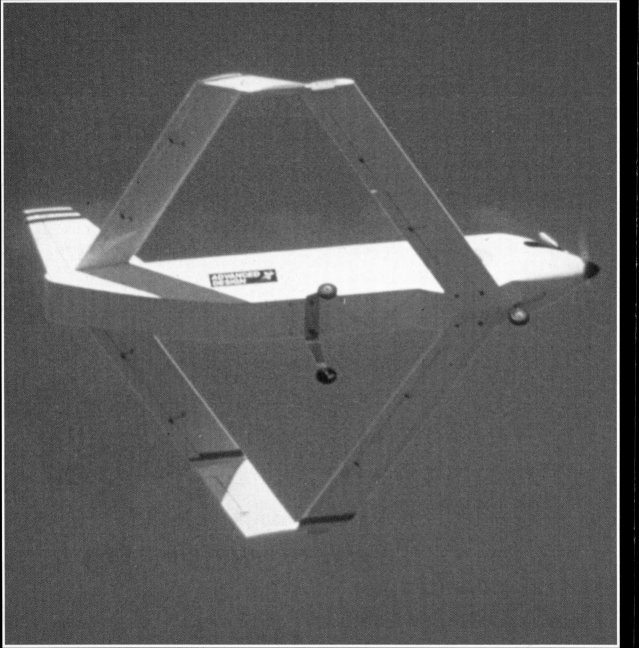

>>> Lighter-than-Air Options <<<

New aerospace technologies have also revived an almost extinct species - the airship.

The *Hindenburg* disaster at Lakehurst, New Jersey in May 1937 spelt the end of serious airship development by the major powers for more than fifty years, but on the eve of a new century, giant helium-filled airships began to take shape in long empty airship sheds.

In the 1990s, the British Army announced its intention to operate a fleet of advanced technology airships capable of carrying up to 30 tonnes of equipment or military personnel. They will be required to operate in areas where conventional fixed and rotary-wing aircraft cannot. They will have to be silent, reliable, safe and cost effective. Unlike a helicopter, which uses large amounts of fuel when it hovers, an airship simply throttles back and floats in one position at altitudes between 2,000-4,000 ft, depending on the wind, for as long as is required. With the composite envelope filled with hundreds of small helium-filled honeycomb cells, bullets or even a missile would pass straight through with little loss of gas.

Although its main role is seen as that of a stealthy airlifter, other more specialised missions are also being seriously considered including Airborne Early Warning (AEW), radio relay over mountainous regions such as the Balkans where communications are often disrupted, maritime and landmine countermeasures and large floating field hospitals. Despite their bulk, gas-filled airships have a low radar signature and with state-of-the-art Radar-Warning-Receivers (RWR) and Electronic Countermeasures (ECM) sensors, the airship should be assured of a high rate of survivability.

There are several contenders for the future British Army airship including Airship Technologies which is proposing its 270 ft-long composite envelope AT-04. Fitted with advanced rotating or fixed phased array UHF radar within the envelope and powered by three 450 hp Diesel Air Ltd engines, two with vectoring ducted propulsors mounted on the gondola and one fixed in the stern, the all-weather, day/night AT-04 would have a maximum speed of 100 mph and a ferry range of over 3,600 miles cruising at 50 mph.

However, at the beginning of the 21st century, the spirit of Count von Zeppelin is not dead. In fact for the first time since the *Graf Zeppelin II* was launched in 1938, the German government is backing the development of giant heavy-lift airships and a new Zeppelin airship has already taken to the air.

The Zeppelin-NT Technics company, headed by one of the Count's descendants Albrecht Graf von Brandenstein-Zeppelin, is developing the 250 ft-long semi-rigid LZ NO7 airship, the first for more than 60 years powered by three vectored-thrust Textron Lycoming piston engines, at Friedrichshafen on the shores of Lake Constance.

A second German airship, but in a different league altogether, is the CL160 *CargoLifter*. Almost 850 ft in length, the semi-rigid CL160, powered by four low-speed vectored thrust diesel engines, it has bow and stern spacecraft-type thrusters for additional manoeuvrability. As its name suggests, the CL160 will have a huge payload of 160 tonnes which would make it an ideal military strategic transport. With a cruising speed of 50-60 mph the *CargoLifter* is designed to have a still-air range of 6,000 miles.

Its unique integrated winch system enables the *CargoLifter* to station itself over pick-up or delivery points and remain airborne during cargo on- and off-loading. Ground support is kept to a minimum, comprising a football pitch-sized operating zone, four tie-down anchor points and water for its computer-controlled ballast tanks which, along with fuel, can be pumped aboard using ground-based systems. No mooring mast is required. The CL160 is optimised to carry a 164 ft-long 'multi-box' container able to carry up to 500 fully equipped troops, three Main Battle Tanks (MBT) or Apache helicopters.

Work is well advanced on construction of the 1,000 ft-long air-conditioned CL160 assembly hangar at Brand, 40 miles south of Berlin, capable of accommodating two *CargoLifters* side-by-side. An American *CargoLifter* operating base is planned at Elizabeth, North Carolina, while the maiden flight of the immense CL160 is scheduled for 2002, with the first series production of up to four airships a year beginning in Germany and the USA two years later.

Above: The Cargolifter CL160, which will be built in Germany and the United States, would make an ideal military airlifter with a 160 tonne payload.

Above: Mi-26 *Hook* and Mi-8 *Hip* helicopters flying over the previously ultra-secret Russian test base at Zhukovskii which has been the venue of international airshows since the fall of the Soviet Union.

If you design an aircraft that is more technologically advanced and capable than that of any of your potential enemies, it has to be developed in complete secrecy. To be able to do this, you have to have a secure airfield in order carry out flight trials and evaluation. An airfield, by its very nature, is not an easy place to secure. It will by necessity have large workshops and hangars and, most revealingly, a long runway.

The facility should be in a remote location, ideally only reached by air transport. Only a few nations with vibrant aerospace industries have been able to achieve this measure of security at their major test facilities.

>>> Peenemunde <<<

Hitler's Germany established a large custom-built research complex at Peenemunde-Karlshagen, a small village on the Baltic coast, in late 1936. Designed primarily for rocket research, many advanced aircraft were developed here during the early war years including the Me 163 *Komet*, and culminating with the pulse-jet V-1 and V-2 'Reprisal' rockets.

August 1933 saw the development of a so-called 'new TsAGI' (Central Institute of Aero and Hydro-Dynamics) near the city of Ramenskoye, 30 miles to the south east of central Moscow. It had a good railway connection with Moscow and plenty of open areas for the construction of laboratories, an airfield and an artificial lake for hydroplanes (flying boats) - the Moscow River flowed nearby.

Above: One of the last ultra-secret aircraft tetsed at Zhukovskii before the end of the soviet Union was the Yak-141 Freestyle.

The first set of new TsAGI wind tunnels was built alongside the institute and by 1939 more than 10,000 people worked at the facility which was given the name Stakhanovo. The airfield's three runways — a 3,350 ft-long VPP-1, 2,500 ft-long VPP-2 and a 2,150 ft-long VPP-3 — corresponded to the requirements of the aircraft of the time. Together with the taxiways and aircraft hard stands, the total area covered with concrete amounted to 300,000_ yds. The lake for hydroplanes was, however, never built. By the autumn of 1939 the airfield was already being expanded with runways lengthened and an innovative 5 ft-high 'ski-jump' constructed at the end of VPP-1 to help heavy aircraft to take off. Auxiliary surfaces were also extended and when Germany attacked the USSR in June 1941, LII airfield already covered an area of 500,000_ yds.

By this time the facility known as the LII (*Lyotnolssledovatelskiy Institut* - Flight Research Institute) was under the command of Soviet chief test pilot Mikhail Gromov. During the war years the airfield served as a base for two heavy bomber divisions which were involved in bombing missions over major German cities including Berlin and Koenigsberg. The institute had been transferred to Kazan and Novosibirsk with only a skeleton staff remaining at Stakhanovo.

Above: Seen at Zhukovskii in mid-winter 1994 during flight testing is the prototype Sukhoi Su-34all-weather attack aircraft.

Immediately after the war, when the jet era began, the airfield was extended to absorbed most of the nearby village of Novoye Syolo. VPP-2 and VPP-3 runways were abandoned, while VPP-1 was extended by 1,500 ft, the 'ski-jump' being demolished in the process, and in June 1950 the construction of the 13,200 ft-long VPP-4 runway was started. On 23 April 1947, a hundred years after the birth of the 'father of Russian Aviation', Nikolay Zhukovskii, Stakhanovo was granted the status of a city and renamed Zhukovskii.

By 1959, VPP-4 had been extended to nearly 18,000 ft which was required in order to flight test a new generation of supersonic aircraft

Above: The Myasishchyev VM-T Atlant, a converted Soviet nuclear bomber, was converted at Zhukovskii to transport large space launchers to Baikonur.

which included the ultra-secret Myasishchyev M-50 *Bounder* supersonic strategic bomber, the Soviet equivalent the US XB-70 *Valkyrie*.

At the beginning of the 1950s an OSP-48 radio instrument landing system (ILS) was installed which was replaced several years later with more modern RSBNAN and Globus-2 radar systems. In 1957 the KDP-2 control tower was put into operation, which was rebuilt and upgraded in 1980. Extensive measuring and navigation systems were also installed in the 1980s including the Platsdarm-1 N microwave instrument landing system (IL compatible with the ICAO requirements.

The first flight test measuring system was created at Zhukovskii airfield in 1946 when a set of German Askania theodolites, US anti-aircraft artillery radar and Soviet designed telemetric stations were installed They were continually upgraded and by the 1960s computer processed data was used for the first time.

At the height of the Cold War, all new Soviet aircraft, civil and military, were flight-tested at Zhukovs At the same time, the US Department of Defense began satellite surveillance of the facility and several new

Above: Developed during the Cold War, the Forward-Swept Wing (FSW)
Sukhoi S-27 Berkut remained under wraps at Zhukovskii until 1997.

types of aircraft were identified. These were given the codename RAM, for Ramenskoye as Zhukovskii was unknown at the time in the West. The prototype Su-24 *Fencer* was RAM-A, the supersonic transport Tu-144 was RAM-H, the first Su-27 *Flanker*, RAM-K and the MiG-29 *Fulcrum* was RAM-L

Since 1975, because of extension of the flight range of aircraft and missiles tested and the need to collect telemetric information during the whole flight test envelope, airborne control and data recording stations were installed in the cabins of LII-based Il-I8S1P aircraft. At the end of 1980s five Il-76 aircraft were converted from military A-SO 'Mainstay' airborne early warning and control aircraft fitted with radar that can track aerial vehicles at a distance of 375 miles and space vehicles at 625 miles. Six experimental vehicles can be traced simultaneously. The Il-76MAs also carries a satellite-based communications and data-link system, which

In 1984 still another test site was constructed at Zhukovskii, a short runway covered with cast iron and steel plates for testing VSTOL take-offs of Yak-38 *Forger* and supersonic Yak-141 *Freestyle* fighters, known initially as RAM-T. Between 1986-1990, VPP-1 runway was rebuilt yet again, changing its lateral profile from a concave to a convex one, and strengthening it with ten layers of concrete making it nearly 6 ft thick in centre!

Above: The Russian fifth-generation FSW S-37 made its first flight from Zhukovskii in September 1997 taking the West by surprise.

Zhukovskii's two runways are capable of operating any aircraft in the world, including a space shuttle. The airfield is used not only by the LII. All the main Russian design bureaux are located there with the exception of Beriev and the Mil and Kamov helicopter bureaux, and it is still used for initial tests of all new Russian aircraft.

In the post-Soviet era some 120,000 people live in Zhukovskii and most are involved to some extent in aviation-related activities. In spite of considerable funding difficulties, the LII airfield, now known as the Gromov Institute, is maintained in good condition. Every two years international MAKS air shows are organised there and the airfield is presently used by several cargo airlines, usually created by the design bureaux, Ilavia (Ilyushin) and Sukhoi Airlines, as well as the Ministry of Emergency Situations. A border post and customs clearance post has also been set up in the airport area.

Although it is no longer one of the West's prime surveillance targets, as it was during the Cold War, it is large and remote enough to keep a number of 'Black' projects, such as the Sukhoi S-37 and MiG 1.44, under wraps for more than five years - and there may be others hidden in one of the hundreds of hangars and assembly shops at Zhukovskii.

Above: A vast array of different Soviet test aircraft can be seen through the Zhukovskii's well-patrolled perimeter fence in 1990.

Above: The CIA's first Lockheed U-2 spyplane, codenamed *Angel*, first flew from Area 51 on 1 August 1955.

>>> Area 51 <<<

Area 51 is the home of America's 'Black' projects, or not as the US government would have us believe. Officially, it does not exist; all knowledge of such a facility is categorically denied.

Situated in a remote lake bed at the foot of Emigrant valley, Nevada, north west of the gambling capital of the world Las Vegas, Area 51 is within the three million acre Nellis bombing and gunnery range which includes Tonapah and White Sands. The number 51 simply refers to an area of land that is part of the Department of Energy's Nevada test site. Geographically it is Groom Lake, to those working within the Nellis range it is 'Dreamland', a reference to all the fantastic aircraft tested at Area 51.

The existence of Area 51 is proof that 'Black' projects exist. A secret flight test centre can have only one purpose, that is to test military aircraft or systems that have highly sensitive operational roles. Only a small number of projects have been made public, the most well known are the U-2, A-12/SR-71, F-117 *Nighthawk* and the *Tacit Blue*.

Area 51 is an impressive sight, with hundreds of buildings on the surface, and it is highly plausible that extensive facilities exist underground. The interesting aspect of Area 51 is the runway. It is over 30,000 ft long - almost six miles. Why? A runway has only one purpose, that is for take-off and landings, and only a high-supersonic or hypersonic craft would require such a length. Could such an aircraft be flying from Area 51?

Above: Ten CIA Mach 3 Lockheed A-12 reconnaissance aircraft, including the sole two-seater *Goose*, at Groom Lake in the early 1960s.

It is of interest that there have been many reports of large sonic booms, strong enough to shake walls and rattle windows, and weird contrails in the shape of doughnut rings. This clearly points to some form of secret testing.

Area 51 can trace its history back to the mid-1950s when it was created by the CIA, and not the US Air Force as commonly thought. The CIA and the Lockheed Skunk Works decided to collaborate on the development of a super spy aircraft to be used against the Soviet Union and WarPac countries. The codename of the project was *Aquatone*. The aircraft became known as the U-2 and was designed to fly above the range of Soviet air defences

Meanwhile, the 'Black' world expanded into space. The Pentagon established the National Reconnaissance Office (NRO) in 1960, although for the next three decades it would technically be a felony to admit that it existed. Its mission was to provide space-based intelligence systems to meet the needs of the CIA, the National Security Agency and the armed forces. As it did so, secret funds amounting to billions of dollars became a permanent feature of the annual USAF budget.

Area 51 was active again and more buildings were built for the ever more ambitious programmes. In 1964 President Lyndon Johnson disclosed the existence of the YF-12 interceptor and the SR-71 strategic reconnaissance aircraft, both related to the A-12 program, the existence of which remained secret until 1982.

Above: After successfully test firing AIM-47 air-to-air missiles, the YF-12A programme was cancelled in February 1968.

Below: Northrop's *Tacit Blue*, a stealth technology aircraft, flew at Groom Lake in complete secrecy for over a decade.

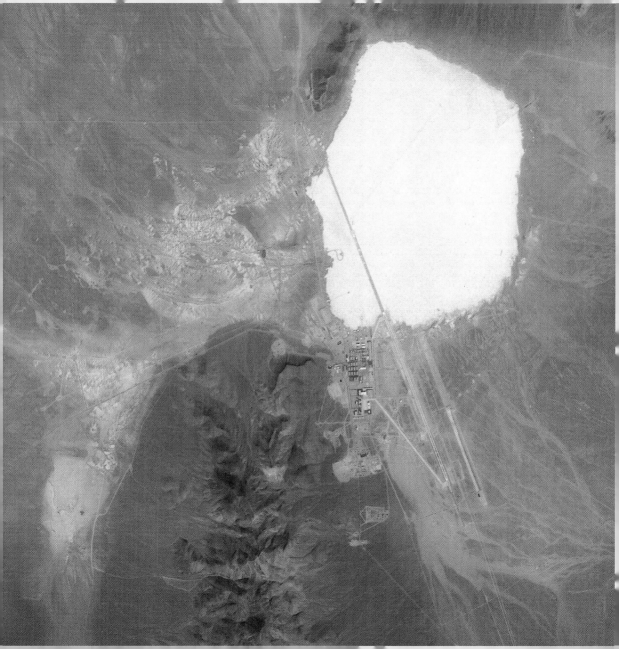

Above: *An artists impression of the Black Knight, a possible replacement for USAF's Lockheed SR-71 Blackbird.*

>>> Billion Dollar Babies <<<

The levels of expenditure at Area 51 are truly awesome. Highly complex accounting procedures cover the tracks of where the dollars go, and anyone who gets close to the truth of what is going on is blocked by severe national security legislation.

By the mid-1980s, spending at Area 51 topped $25 billion dollars per year but, as the levels of expenditure were never broken down into individual programmes, it was impossible to analyse the results.

During this period much work was done expanding the facilities of Area 51. New administration buildings and hangars were built, and 90,000 acres of public land to the east of the complex was purchased to prevent members of the public observing the complex.

Local aviation spotters are known as 'Groomers' and live for the day they can photograph or film a secret project, even if it is against the law. To keep them at bay, a highly sophisticated network of cameras, ground

Above: The next generation of USAF's hypersonic strike aircraft, based on the X-43A HyperSoar, will be tested at Area 51.

sensors, helicopters and ground vehicles provide a comprehensive security system. If you have not got the message that you are not welcome by now, then maybe the signs warning 'use of deadly force authorised' may help emphasise the point.

The ground force of civilian security guards drive around the surrounding areas in white jeeps wearing desert combat fatigues known affectionately as 'Cammo Dudes' by the 'Groomers'. A news reporter recently tried to over-fly the base in a light aircraft but was buzzed by an F-16 fighter within seconds of entering the Area 51 airspace and arrested on landing his aircraft.

Above: Built at the 'Skunk Works' and tested at Area 51, the Lockheed F-117A Nighthawk 'Stealth Fighter'.

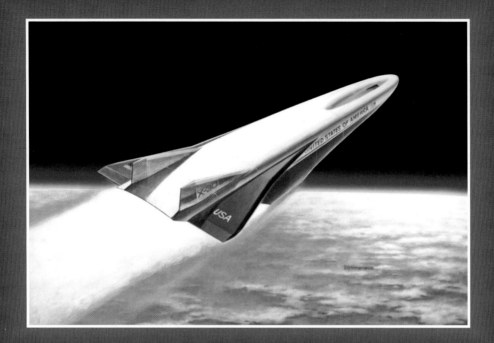

Above: Billions of dollars were spent on developing the X-30 National Aero Space Plane (NASP) project that was canceled in 1992.

The base now comes under the control of the USAF since almost 40% of its budget is spent on research and development and much of it at the facility. This spending is concealed in many ways. Programme titles such as Advanced Program Evaluation (APE) cover many projects and devour over a billion dollars alone. Other non-specific programmes account for another $450 million, many of which originate at both the Lockheed Martin Skunk Works and Boeing's Phantom Works.

'Black' programmes are extremely lucrative to aerospace manufacturers and allow projects to take place that under normal conditions would never happen. The B-2A Stealth bombers cost over $1 billion dollars each and despite their impressive debut in the recent Kosovo conflict, it is doubtful that Congress would ever have approved the funding to allow such a project, conceived during the Cold War, to continue. This gives the USAF even more justification to indulge in 'Black' programmes and the Clinton Administration was very supportive of Area 51's activities with no sign in letting up on the massive budgets currently being allocated for both 'Black' and 'White' military projects.

>>> Hiding The Dollars <<<

It is not uncommon for different 'Black' programme offices to be working on similar projects, thereby duplicating effort and wasting money. This problem was highlighted in 1995 in a report that condemned the overlap of work, and demonstrated that the government had in fact on several occasions paid for the same work to be done by several different project offices or companies. The situation came to a head during the lawsuit between the government, General Dynamics and McDonnell Douglas over the cancellation of the A-12 *Avenger II* programme in 1991. It was later revealed that had the project been given access to stealth technology developed for other programmes, the *Avenger* would not have been cancelled.

The US Department of Defense (DoD) concedes that the 'Black' programmes are complex, expensive and difficult to quantify, and they even concede that, at times, attempts have been made to confuse and mislead the public. It will not, however, agree to reform a system that has for almost 40 years "protected" America's national interests.

Above: Early F-117A 'stealth fighters were test flown at Groom Lake before being moved to nearby Tonopah when the first squadron was formed.

The Clinton administration planned to spend $4.96 billion on classified research and development programmes in the fiscal year 2001, mostly destined for the USAF 'Black' projects that are formally known within the DoD as unacknowledged Special Access Programs (SAPs), all of which have to be approved of by the Secretary of Defense or his deputy.

SAPs are deemed of such high value that they cannot be protected by normal classification measures. They are on a "need to know" basis, which minimises access to critical information and reduces leakage of any project or its purpose.

It is well known that the then head of the USAF denied all knowledge of the Stealth programmes before their public unveiling. This was probably true and indicates how sensitive security is. SAPs report to the services, DoD and Congress through special channels that involve the minimum of personnel.

In 1997 a report from the Senate commission admitted to around 150 DoD-approved SAPs,

Above: The F-117A 'Stealth Fighter' being prepared for its next mission.

divided into three categories - Acquisition (AQ-SAP), Operations/Support (OS-SAP) and Intelligence (IN-SAP) - which in turn are then divided between acknowledged and unacknowledged groups. A new government committee, known as the SAP Oversight Committee (SAPOC), has been set up to ensure none of them overlap with each other. Even with these controls, some of the most secret 'Black' projects are omitted from the SAPOC, thus creating an inner sanctum of very few privileged people who know exactly what is going on at any given time.

Having such intense security also brings its own problems. It has recently been estimated that almost 40% of all 'Black' project costs are for security alone.

>>> The Truth Is Out There <<<

The truth of what is going on at Area 51 is out there, but most of it will never be revealed to the public. The USAF has been very successful in covering its tracks, and only when it decides that a project should be made public, does it happen.

The facility has been featured in numerous magazines and newspapers over the past four decades, and TV shows such as the *X-Files* have a particular interest in the activities of Area 51.

One good indication of the activity of Area 51 is the *Janet* flights. These are scheduled flights that take staff to and from Area 51 using Boeing 737s and CT-43s operating under the call sign *Janet*. They operate from a specially built terminal at Las Vegas airport, and can fly as many as 12 flights per day. Assuming that each aircraft carries an average of 100 people per flight, this would indicate intense activity at Area 51. A typical programme employs some 200 staff; these are broken down into small units that work only on specific projects. It is conceivable that most members of the work teams do not get to see the aircraft that they are working on, and that systems are removed from the trials aircraft for routine maintenance, thus keeping those who actually need to see the aircraft to an absolute minimum.

>>> 'Black' Flight Profile <<<

A typical long distance 'Black' mission would begin with a take-off in darkness from Area 51, followed by a maximum rate climb to high altitude, to minimise noise and the risk of being seen. The aircraft will then air-refuel from a tanker with specially screened aircrew, and a flight profile will probably take it to one of the UK's few 'Black Holes', RAF Machrihanish in Scotland. This remote location features an extensive complex of buildings, hangars and a very long runway, way beyond the normal RAF requirements in the UK. It was rumoured that the US paid for most of these facilities to accommodate 'Black' programme aircraft and the airfield was certainly used by USAF SR-71 *Blackbirds* during the Cold War. A detachment of US Navy SEALS (Special Forces) operates from the base and could provide close security if the need should arise. Several sightings have been made of unusual looking aircraft types flying from this base by several different sources, including commercial airliner's flight crews, a North Sea oil rig and high-intensity sonic boom tracking by measuring stations in Holland.

Because of the time differences, an aircraft flying from the US West Coast could arrive in the UK in darkness providing excellent cover for 'Black' operations. RAF Machrihanish is well away from built-up areas and on the few nearby islands only a small population exists. After refuelling, the aircraft could return to Area 51 again in darkness avoiding any of the 'Groomers' who may be waiting.

>>> In The Wings <<<

One thing that is certain is the fact that when the US removes any aircraft from service, there is always a replacement waiting in the wings, and its only a question of time when it is released for service - and public view. The USAF is currently suffering from a problem. In the UK it is described as 'Shiny Kit Syndrome', where 'Black' programme engineers and managers decide that the aircraft or system they are developing is so secret and valuable that it cannot be used for fear of loss or even being revealed to a potential enemy.

Another aspect of this problem was highlighted by a 1995 commission, which pointed out that a breakthrough in military technology is limited if their own commanders do not know how to use it. The report alleged that the SAP community keeps field commanders in the dark until the systems are ready for use. They are then put under such tight constraints that they are unable to use the technology in any practical way.

A joint staff senior officer commented that: "We still treat certain capabilities as pearls too precious to wear. We acknowledge their value, but because of their value, we lock them up and don't use them for fear of losing them."

The recent Gulf and Kosovo conflicts highlighted several areas of operational capability where there was a shortfall in performance by the USAF. In the first, what commanders lacked was the real time reconnaissance capability of the SR-71, which had been retired only nine months earlier. The North Korean crisis of 1994 even led to the *Blackbird* being returned to service in 1996, only for it to be finally grounded a year later with no replacement being revealed.

It is of interest that the USAF retired one of its best strike aircraft, the F-111, after the Gulf War (*Desert Storm*) and again, no replacement was acknowledged. Could it be that a replacement is in existence, but that we have not seen it?

Clearly both of these valuable types will be replaced, possibly by small numbers of highly specialised 'Black' aircraft that could operate from continental United States to any theatre in the world without the requirement to land in a foreign country. Such an aircraft may explain the speedy retirement of the F-111 and unconfirmed reports of a slender blended variable-geometry 'switchblade' wing design seen flying over Britain's North Sea may provide an answer.

The USAF has made no secret of the fact that it wants an aircraft with the speed of the B-1B *Lancer*, stealth qualities of the B-2A *Spirit*, and the bomb-carrying capability of the mighty B-52. This would be a 'White' project or acknowledged as an SAP by DoD definition. However, it is possible that in the recent past such a project existed, or still exists, as a 'Black' programme and although the costs of such a project would be enormous, even by US standards, what the USAF wants, it usually gets.

One interesting outcome of the analysis of the Kosovo conflict was that of the information war. Intelligence played a critical role and the gathering of information plays a major part in operational planning. Many methods are used ranging from space-based satellites to low-flying, relatively unsophisticated UAVs. In Kosovo the main problem the US faced was in having too much information, so much that it took days to process and analyse instead of hours. This meant that targets originally found had moved by the time aircraft were assigned to destroy them.

The losses of Serbian tanks and other military materiel were far lower than claimed by NATO Forces at the height of the conflict. Although the USAF had the use of the J-STARS airborne surveillance aircraft during the conflict, it was felt that a smaller, more stealthy aircraft could have gained better results. This is interesting because one of the Area 51 'Black' projects revealed in 1996 was the Northrop *Tacit Blue*, a prototype stealth battlefield surveillance aircraft which made its last operational flight in 1985.

Was an operational development built? If it was, why was it not used in Kosovo or could it be that this conflict was deemed too much of a risk to expose such an aircraft to the combat theatre? Remember, the Serbs managed to down the first F-117A Stealth fighter. There has, however, been continuing speculation and rumours of high-performance high altitude stealth reconnaissance platforms known variously as Aurora, said to be powered by Pulse Detonation Wave (PWE) engines, and ASTRA.

Above: USAF wants a bomber with the speed of the B-1B Lancer, seen here, the stealth of the
B-2A Spirit and the weapons load of the B-52 Stratofortress - is it flying yet at Area 51.

An acronym for Advanced Stealth Reconnaissance Aircraft, ASTRA is claimed to be an advanced development of the Northrop/McD YF-23, the unsuccessful competitor for the USAF Advanced Tactical Fighter competition. Using *Tacit Blue* technology, also a Northrop programme, a small batch of ASTRAs were possibly constructed at the company's Advanced Technology and Design Center and flight-tested at Area 51.

On 29 September 1994, it was reported that ASTRA AV-6 made an emergency landing at Boscombe Down, Britain's high security test and evaluation airfield. Although the incident was denied by both the DoD and UK Ministry of Defence, observers believe that it represented additional evidence of another, as yet unacknowledged 'Black' programme.

Another possible programme being trialed at Area 51 could be a large UAV, possibly a scaled-up version of the cancelled *DarkStar* flying-wing project. The USAF recently stated that no target is worth a pilot's life. This of course is true and may explain the huge push on developing Unmanned Combat Air Vehicle (UCAVs) technologies.

Some if not all of the UFO reports received in and around America, and the Western States in particular, are probably UAVs or UCAVs on flight evaluation missions. Their shapes are generally unconventional and, to the untrained eye, these would indeed seem to be 'from another planet'.

Although there are many rumours regarding crashed alien spacecraft being stored at Area 51, and indeed reverse engineering being carried out to give us information on advanced technologies, it should be left to Mulder and Scully out of the fictitious *X-Files* to get to the bottom of such stories.

Whatever your views are of Area 51 and its 'Black' programmes, there are two clear conclusions. The first is that Area 51 has been a secure base for some of the world's most spectacular aerospace projects, both acknowledged and unacknowledged. And secondly, for all the criticism directed

Right: Although it flew before in 1945, the Gotha Go 229, the world's first 'stealth' jet fighter-bomber, never saw operational service.

A USAF real-time analysis of air combat in Vietnam, called 'The Red Baron Study', showed that over half of the aircrews shot down were unaware of their attackers. Available data showed that same experience to be true in World Wars One and Two, and in Korea. Biographies of fighter aces are full of references that credit their success to an ability to see their opponents before they are seen themselves - attacking out of the sun and from their adversary's blind spot. A stealthy or low observable approach was recommended!

As detection techniques have evolved, so have detection avoidance techniques. The development of effective radar networks by Britain in the early days of World War Two led to stealth counters and radar-absorbing materials initially used by Germany on submarine periscopes and air-breathing U-boat snorkels in the 1940s.

Germany later incorporated radar-evading shapes and materials into advanced tailless designs such as the Horton Ho IX, the Gotha P-60B and Lippisch LP 13A, although some of these were discovered more by accident than design. Due to shortage of materials, including aluminium, large supersonic flying-wing bomber projects such as the Junkers EF 130 and Focke-Wulf 1000, had to be built largely of wood, the outcome of which was a very small radar cross section (RCS).

After the war, some of these lessons were taken on board by US designers, although the accepted wisdom of the period was the higher the speed, the lower the observability. More sophisticated stealth techniques were later applied to surveillance drones including the Ryan Q-2 *Firebee* and Lockheed D-21, while Boeing applied stealth technologies to its supersonic Short-Range Attack Missile (SRAM) in the late 1960s.

General Dynamics (GD) was also a major player in the early days of stealth, building the prototype for the USAF's first radar antenna target scattering facility known as RatScat, in White Sands, New Mexico, which was used in the 1970s to measure accurately the radar cross section (RSC) of aircraft. In the late 1950s, GD pursued a highly stealthy design concept to meet requirements set by the

Above: US Army technicians examine the partly completed second prototype Gotha Go 229 at discovered at Leipzig at the end of the war.

Above: A special pressure-suit was designed for pilots flying Germany's Gotha Go 229 flying-wing jet fighter-bomber.

Above: The Gotha Go 229 was powered by two Jumo turbojets blended into the flying wing.

Above: Horten's last flying-wing design, the Ho XVC high-performance sailplane, was eventually built in Argentina in 1949.

Central Intelligence Agency (CIA) for a supersonic high-altitude reconnaissance aircraft to replace the Lockheed U-2. The design began as a B-58 parasite known as 'Super Hustler', and evolved into an independent aircraft optimised to cruise at 125,000 feet at a speed of Mach 6.25. This configuration, dubbed 'Kingfish', was to be built mostly of a heat-resistant and radar-attenuating ceramic material known as pyroceram. Two Marquardt ramjets powered the aircraft in the cruise portion of its mission with two retractable turbojets providing power for take-off and acceleration to speeds at which the ramjets could be ignited.

The radical GD design, however, lost out to its Lockheed competitor, the single-seat A-12, the forerunner of the two-seat USAF aircraft more widely recognised as the SR-71 *Blackbird*. The A-12 is credited with being the first operational aircraft to incorporate stealth to a high degree in its original design. Canted tails, saw-toothed structure, pie-shaped panels on leading and trailing edges, blended wings and chines, and radar-absorbing structure and paint combined to reduce the aircraft's radar cross section to a small fraction of its contemporaries.

Lockheed took stealth, or low observable (LO) technology to an even higher level in the 1970s when it combined computer technology with some obscure mathematical formulae relating to the reflection of electromagnetic radiation. The resulting computer programme called 'Echo' could accurately predict the way a flat-surfaced object would appear on radar. The company applied the software in a Defense Advanced Research Projects Agency (DARPA) study to create the *Have Blue* aircraft, a small faceted aircraft with tails canted inboard, the predecessor of the F-117A 'Stealth Fighter'.

Above: Paralelling the Horten brother's flying-wing concepts, was American Jack Northrop whose jet-powered Northrop MX-324 flew in 1945.

These aircraft, developed under Project *Senior Trend*, flew only at night for almost eight years in conditions that were very demanding for the pilots and their families. So secret was the project, that daylight flights were deemed to risky and could compromise the programme.

The level of secrecy was incredible even in the 'Black' world. When an F-117A *Nighthawk* crashed in the desert, the entire area was sealed off and every piece of the local crash scene was sifted to remove any parts of the aircraft, however small. The aircraft's Radar Absorbing Material (RAM) coating was then highly secret and even today is still classified.

When the F-117A was finally revealed to the public in 1988, it had been in operation for more than five years. The recent Kosovo crisis highlighted the value of stealth aircraft that can penetrate highly sophisticated integrated air defence systems. Ironically, the USAF lost only two aircraft to Serbian surface-to-air missiles (SAM), one of which was an F-117A *Nighthawk*, the other being a 'non stealthy' F-16 *Falcon*.

The faceted design of Lockheed's F-117 was very successful at breaking up and scattering the aircraft's radar image, but it imposed serious performance limitations on the aircraft. The F-117A is a subsonic platform with a small internal weapons bay. Its complicated airframe is a nightmare to maintain and its RAM-covered surface can actually be damaged by rain.

Above: Lockheed's F-117A Nighthawk was dubbed the 'Stealth Fighter' when it was revealed to the public in 1988.

Above: The facetted construction of the Lockheed F-117A Nighthawk, designed to scatter its radar image, can clearly be seen.

Above: When 'dirty' - with its landing gear extended, the F-117A Nighthawk's stealth is compromised.

A completely different approach to a stealth concept was taken by the designers of the USAF's 'Stealth Bomber', the Northrop B-2A *Spirit*. Project *Senior CJ* began in 1978 with both Lockheed and Northrop as contenders for the contract for a LO intercontinental range bomber. It was won by Northrop, which would be the prime contractor, with Boeing, General Dynamics and Vought forming the team to produce the new aircraft.

After trialing thousands of RCS images at the Northrop Radar Cross Section facility at Tejon Canyon near Palmdale, California, a unique blended flying-wing design was selected, a concept that can be traced back to the 1940s. The Austrian Dr Alexander Lippisch had experimented with tailless delta-wing gliders in the 1920s and was later responsible for the *Luftwaffe's* first rocket-powered interceptor, the Me 163, still the only tailless fighter to be mass produced. The tailless concept gave a compact airframe the lowest drag and weight for the largest wing area and the Me 163 also had a very low RCS.

dust and could theoretically outmanoeuvre any other fighter of the day. It was never flown but Dr Lippisch went to the United States after the war as part of Operation *Paperclip* and in 1947 worked closely on the Convair XP-92, a mixed jet/rocket delta-wing interceptor that led directly to the USAF's successful F-102A *Delta Dagger* and F-106A *Delta Dart* Century fighters.

Even more significant were the German Horton brothers who were building flying-wing gliders, with no rudder or tailplane, before the war. After many trials and tribulations,

Above: Germany's World War Two Me 163 Komet, designed by Dr Alexander Lippisch, is still the world's only operational tailless fighter.

Above: The world's first tailless jet-bomber, the Northrop YB-49 entered USAF service in 1949.

Above: Forty years after the YB-49, Northrop Grumman's B-2A Spirit 'Stealth Bomber' flew for the first time.

Above: USAF's B-2A Spirit low-observable strategic penetration bomber with serrated bomb bay door open.

they designed the advanced Horton Ho IX, a supersonic twin-jet flying-wing fighter bomber which went into production as the Gotha Go 229A in 1945. The blended flying-wing had its two Jumo turbojets mounted above the wing and carried weapons in an internal bay. The large, nose-mounted cockpit was fitted with an ejector seat and the airframe was mainly constructed of wood mixed with resin. It would have been almost invisible to contemporary airborne and air defence radar. Only one flew before the war ended. Although US troops captured the prototype and the Soviets overran the Gotha works and with it plans for the even more advanced P-60B *Nachtjager* (Nightfighter), few post-war tailless or flying-wing aircraft saw the light of day.

In England, the de Havilland company used German research data to produce the DH 108, a small, single-seat tailless jet which broke up in mid-air while attempting to break the absolute air speed record in September 1946, killing the test pilot, Geoffrey de Havilland Jnr. A prototype flying-wing jet bomber, the AW 52, was flown in 1947 but the combination of high cost and low performance killed the project.

Above: Ryan experimented with a stealthy tailless unmanned aerial vehicle (UAV) known as the *Manta Ray* in the 1970s.

More successful was Northrop's family of flying-wing warplanes. Jack Northrop was working in parallel with Dr Lippisch and the Horton brothers in the 1930s, convinced that a flying-wing low drag could fly faster, further and more economically than conventional aircraft. His company built a number of flying-wing research aircraft during World War Two, culminating in the XP-79B jet fighter prototype and the awesome 172 ft-wingspan XB-35 bomber prototype which, coincidentally, bore a remarkable resemblance to the German Junkers EF 130, a four jet-engined flying-wing strategic bomber projects. The huge bomber was finally put into production and more than a dozen had been built by 1948 when the Air Force decided to replace its four piston engines with eight Allison turbojets. The only YB-49 to be converted broke up in flight over the Mojave Desert after which the

Above: A USAF B-2A Spirit of Air Combat command comes into land using its distinctive trailing-edge elevons.

Above: The DH 108 Swallow research aircraft was the first British supersonic aircraft when it flew in 1946.

Above: Covered in Radar absorbing Material (RAM), the tailless Spirit looks ungainly on the ground.

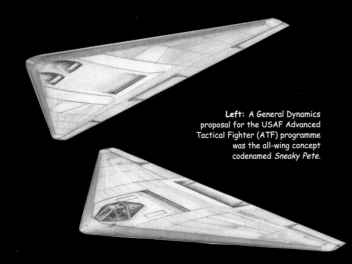

Left: A General Dynamics proposal for the USAF Advanced Tactical Fighter (ATF) programme was the all-wing concept codenamed *Sneaky Pete*.

programme was cancelled in 1949. Although the flying qualities of the flying-wing bomber were excellent, they were expensive to manufacture and had to be fitted with several original control devices to overcome its inherent longitudinal instability. In fact, two of America's top test pilots, Harry Crosby and Glen Edwards, after whom the Muroc Air Field was re-named, lost their lives flying the Northrop XP-79 and YB-49 respectively. The concept would lie dormant for almost 40 years before computerised flight-control systems and composite materials gave it new life.

The reasons for choosing the blended high-aspect flying-wing configuration for Project *Senior CJ* were much the same as those used by

Above: Developed from *Sneaky Pete*, was the GD/McD A-12 Avenger II designed to replace USN A-6 and USAF F-111 strike aircraft.

Above: Stealth technology developed by the highly classified *Tacit Blue* was used for the *Senior CJ* project - the B-2A.

the Horten brothers for their Gotha 229. It is both aerodynamically efficient, which improves range, payload and take-off and landing performance, and is structurally efficient because of the span-wise distribution of weight. This produces a lightly loaded structure, which means very high manoeuvrable loads can be achieved without resorting to excessively heavy construction.

More importantly to the *Senior CJ* project was the flying-wing's very low RCS due to the lack of vertical surfaces. The blended shape minimises radar returns due to scattering at discontinuities in the surface curvature. An added bonus of the blended wing is that it gives greatest structural depth exactly where it is required. The wing root bending moment causes the highest loading on the airframe while the deep wing root also provides a stiff structure that allows lower stress and deflection compared with an unblended structure. This increases the fatigue life of the airframe.

When Project *Senior CJ* was finally revealed to the public at Air Force Plant 42 at Palmdale in 1988 as Air Vehicle-One, later designated by the USAF as B-2A, it had almost exactly the same wingspan as the Northrop YB-49, but the shape of the Gotha 229. With its crew cabin close to the leading edge, its four turbojets were buried deep into the flying wing's shoulders with exhausts above the wing. To dissipate the gases and prevent contrails, chloro-fluorosulphonic acid was injected into the exhaust. However, the B-2A Spirit had been developed during the Cold War and when it entered service 15 years after the Advanced Tactical Bomber (ATB) programme had begun, the Warsaw Pact had ceased to be a threat. Only 21 B-2As were produced, at a cost of more than $1 billion each, and, like the F-117A, its RAM was liable to degrade in prolonged rain!

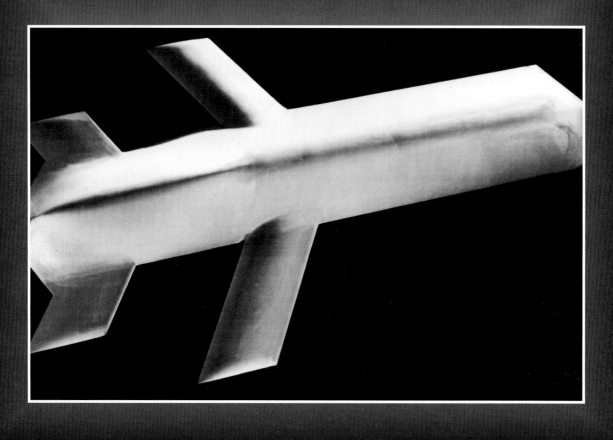

Above: The design of the US Tri-Service Standoff Attack Missile (TSSAM) bears a close resemblance to *Tacit Blue*.

It is clear, however, that the project spawned other 'Black' flying-wing programmes including several UAVs and the much rumoured Northrop Grumman TR-3 *Manta*, developed to meet USAF's Tactical High-Altitude Penetrator (THAP) requirement.

Other projects running alongside the ATB in the 1970s were the USAF's Advanced Tactical Fighter (ATF) and the Navy's Advanced Tactical Aircraft programmes. General Dynamics studied a wide range of ATF concepts, one of which was a highly stealthy, all-wing concept code-named *Sneaky Pete*. This was a tailless delta which evolved under a 'Black' project into a contender for the ATA program which was designed as a stealthy replacement for USN A-6 *Intruders* and USAF F-111 strike aircraft. Designated A-12, to deliberately confuse observers with the Lockheed's A-12 reconnaissance aircraft of two decades earlier, it became known as the 'Dorito' as its shape

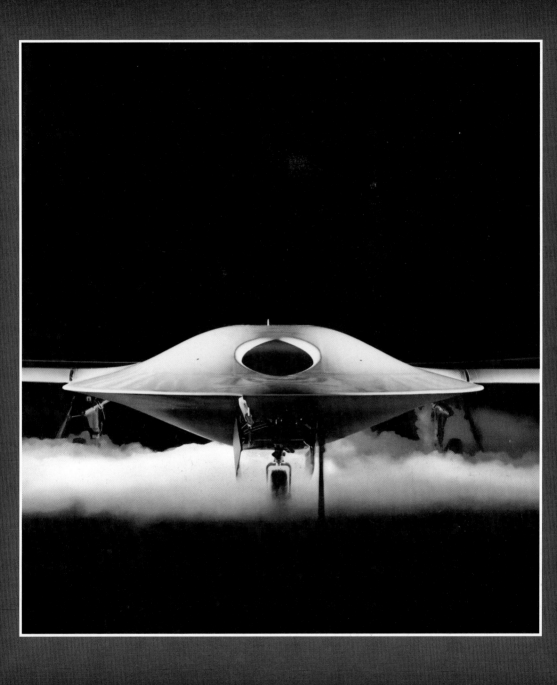

Above: The most stealthy surveillance UAV yet revealed was the Lockheed Martin DarkStar medium-range endurance (MAE) cancelled in 1999.

Above: A 'golden' model DarkStar mounted on a pylon at the Tejon Radar Cross Section (RCS) facility at Palmdale.

cancelled in 1991 before the first aircraft was completed due to spiralling costs and receding in-service dates. Billions of dollars had been sunk into the project and it was widely accepted that hidden under the A-12 programme were other deep 'Black' projects.

So why do these advanced stealth aircraft that are invisible to radar require additional cloaking devices? The reason for this is that, contrary to popular belief, stealth aircraft are not invisible to radar; they just give a smaller radar footprint. This brings its own problems. Because of this fact, a good radar operator can pick out stealth aircraft and target them accordingly. Pilots of stealth aircraft can sometimes become a little complacent and fly similar flight missions over enemy territory, as may have happened to the F-117 *Nighthawk* in Kosovo, in the belief that they cannot be seen.

Decades of stealth technology has been highly refined and should any 'Black' project have

Above: USAF Lockheed Martin F-22 Raptors are being applied with an anti-infra-red (IR) paint known as 'Top Coat'.

Above: A low-observable tailless Unmanned Combat Aerial Vehicle (UCAV) concept from Lockheed Martin.

progressed to a technology demonstrator programme it will be protected by the most advanced cloaking devices. Unconfirmed reports from 'Groomers' around Area 51 have stated that, in daylight hours, they have heard the sound of a jet aircraft above them yet seen only a blurred faint image that could not be identified. This could be made possible by the use of highly powerful electronic currents being passed around the airframe to create a distorted image. There is also a counter-illumination system designed to reduce an aircraft's shape against a bright sky. A concept such as this was used in World War Two, code-named Project *Yehudi*, by RAF Sunderland

Above: A mix of stealthy tailless manned and unmanned aircraft is the vision of the future digitilized battlefield.

aircraft's wings, they could be brightened or dimmed depending on the surrounding sky and this enabled the aircraft to sneak up on an enemy submarine on the surface without being seen. Area 51 is also known to have tested visual stealth methods as part of the original *Have Blue* programme, but both prototypes crashed before the USAF was able to try out this technology.

As already mentioned the USAF has been experimenting with other cloaking devices and by this time the systems

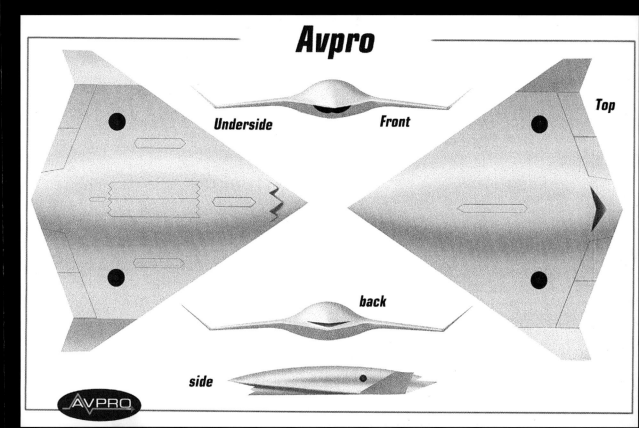

Avpro

Underside

Front

Top

back

side

Above: Running in the face of Western fourth generation fighter design philosophy is the Russian Sukhoi S-37 Forward-Swept Wing prototype.

In the age of television warfare, there is one battle that even CNN will miss - covert warfare waged by Special Forces (SF).

Covert operations have been carried out by small specialist units since the dawn of conflict. During World War Two it was Britain's Special Operations Executive (SOE) and the US Office of Strategic Services (OSS), covert organisations that operated in occupied Europe and the Far East. Their 'Cold War' successors, the Special Air Service (SAS) and Central Intelligence Agency (CIA) respectively developed covert warfare to a high art form and led to the formation of a plethora of other SF units including the 'Green Berets', Navy SEALS, the Special Boat Service (SBS) and 'Delta Force'.

Although these Special Forces are trained to operate behind enemy lines where they are virtually self-sufficient, all have to rely on air power at some time or another for intelligence, insertion, support and extraction. During the Korean War, Special Forces relied on Air Force photo-reconnaissance and transport but it was not until the South East Asia conflict that they began to be assigned dedicated air units.

Above: Special Forces exit from their V-22 Osprey tiltrotor which combines the speed of a fixed-wing aircraft and the vertical take-off capability of a helicopter.

The CIA was already a veteran of covert operations and its role was exposed during Operation *Overflight* when a CIA Lockheed U-2C high-altitude reconnaissance aircraft piloted by Gary Powers was shot down near Sverdlovsk by an SA-2 surface-to-air missile (SAM) on 1 May 1960.

To enable it carry out covert overflights in the future without them being featured in the world's newspaper headlines, the CIA moved its U-2 detachment to Taiwan before an even more potent 'Black' reconnaissance aircraft came within the Agency's sphere of operations. As the world's first operational Mach 3 combat aircraft, the A-12, developed in the early 1960s by the Lockheed Skunk Works, was deployed to Kadena Air Base at Okinawa, Japan, in May 1965. From where they flew Operation *Black Shield* missions over China, North Korea and North Vietnam until 5 June 1968. Its role was then taken over by USAF SR-71 *Blackbird*, a two seat development of the A-12, but the Agency continued in the covert reconnaissance business with Project *Tagboard* until 1971. *Tagboard* was a supersonic drone carried 'piggy back' on the A-12 but was cancelled after only four partially successful missions over China.

Above: A USAF CH-3 recovers an Unmanned Firebee after its covert reconnaissance mission over North Vietnam.

While the CIA continued its airborne activities by operating the largest airline in the world at the time, Air America, to cover its spying operations in South East Asia until the fall of Saigon in May 1975, the US Army Special Operations Forces (SOF) became more involved in counter-insurgency (COIN) missions in Vietnam. By this time USAF HH-3 'Jolly Green Giant' and HH-53 'Super Jolly Green Giant' helicopters, which gained their nicknames from the jungle green camouflage scheme worn in South East Asia, air refuelled by MC-130 *Combat Talons* and escorted by A-1 *Skyraiders*, code-named *Sandies*, were supporting a whole range of SOF operations. These ranged from PoW rescue missions, covert ground reconnaissance to Operation *Buffalo Hunter*, the recovery of unmanned Ryan *Firebees* returning from clandestine reconnaissance missions over North Vietnam and China.

Established in 1977 was US Special Forces Operational Detachment Delta, known as 'Delta Force', a specialist anti-terrorist hostage rescue group. Inspired by the Britain's SAS, one of 'Delta Force's' first mission was Operation *Eagle Claw*, the rescue of American hostages held in the US Embassy in Tehran by Iranian militants in April 1980. In the event, the mission was a disaster. With an unwieldy mix of 'Delta Force', US Army Special

Above: The high-dash speed and hover capability of the CV-22 Osprey makes it an ideal Combat Search and Rescue (CSAR) asset.

Above: Ordered for the three US services, the Osprey tiltrotor is in line to be operated by the British Royal Marine Commandos.

Forces, SEALS, US Navy and Marine helicopters and USAF MC-130s involved, command and control was a nightmare. Three MH-53s went unserviceable en route to a desert rendezvous and another collided with a *Hercules* on lift-off from the airstrip *Desert One*. The operation was cancelled.

As a direct result of the failure of Operation *Eagle Claw*, the US Counter-Terrorist Joint Task Force (CTJTF) came into being at Fort Bragg, bringing together elements of 'Delta Force', US Navy SEALS, USAF 1st Special Operations Wing (SOW) and the US Army's ultra secret 160th Special Operations Aviation Regiment (SOAR).

In the last two decades, covert warfare has risen up the ladder of military planners' priorities. Operation *Desert Storm*, Somalia and the ongoing Balkan conflicts have seen more men and equipment being utilised in covert operations. The recently established Air Force Special Operations Command (AFSOC) at Hurlburt Field, Florida, flew both active and passive roles in the Gulf War. EC-130E Commando Solos of the Air National Guard (ANG) Special Operations Command (SOC) flew 'psychops' missions, interrupting TV and radio stations and

Above: The Osprey's little brother, the Bell-Boeing 609 would be an ideal Special Forces and CSAR platform.

broadcasting Allied news and propaganda, while the fearsome AC-130A *Spectre* gunship operated by AFSOC's 16th Special Operations Squadron (SOS) undertook clandestine attack missions against enemy positions.

Although Air Force Special Operations Command's primary mission is to provide unconventional warfare, direct action, special reconnaissance and counter-terrorism support to US Special Operations Command (SOCOM), Combat Search and Rescue (CSAR) is almost of equal importance in contemporary Out Of Area (OOA) operations.

Having been established during the Vietnam war, Search and Rescue Task Forces (SARTF) remain the core of AFSOC's CSAR operations although fully night-capable MH-53J *Pave Low III* and MH-60G *Pave Hawk* helicopters have replaced the HH-3 'Jolly Green Giants'. During the Gulf War, a SARTF MH-53J rescued a downed US Navy F-14 *Tomcat* pilot 30 miles from Baghdad in broad daylight with A-10 *Warthogs* playing the *Sandy* role. During the UN

Operation *Restore Hope* in Somalia, MH-60 *Pave Hawks* assigned to the US Army's 160th Special Operations Aviation Regiment (SOAR) rescued surviving crew of two Army *Black Hawks* bought down by rebel militia ground fire, but by this time the death, capture and public parading of captured aircrew had become politically unacceptable to NATO governments, and the general public. The prompt safe return of downed aircrew became a military priority. This was graphically illustrated on 2June 1995 when USAF F-16 pilot

Above: Future US Army Special Operations rotary wing assets will use advanced technology developed for the RAH-66 Comanche.

Captain Scott O'Grady was shot down by a Bosnian Serb SAM during Operation *Deny Flight*. Having evaded capture for six days, Captain O'Grady's transmissions from his digital Personnel Locator System (PLS) were picked up by an AWACS aircraft and a successful combined service CSAR mission was undertaken comprising a pair of USMC CH-53s escorted by Marine Corps AH-1W *SuperCobra Sandies* with top cover from F/A-18D *Hornets* and EA-6B *Prowlers* for Suppression of Enemy Defences (SEAD).

NATO CSAR assets were again in action in Yugoslavia in the opening days of Operation *Allied Force*. On the night of 27 March 1999, the USAF lost its first F-117A *Nighthawk* brought down by Yugoslav SAMs 45 miles north west of Belgrade. The pilot ejected successfully and landed some five miles from the crash site. Almost immediately a combined CSAR mission swung into action with eight helicopters led by two AFSOC MH-53J *Pave Low IIIs* from their forward base at Tuzla in Bosnia. Top cover was provided by F-15 and F-16 *Sandies* but with all of these sophisticated assets being bought to bear, it still took some seven hours before a textbook recovery of the pilot was completed. On 2 May, a USAF F-16 suffered an engine failure and crashed during a night mission over north west Serbia. The pilot again ejected successfully and was rescued 11 miles east of Kozluk by an Allied CSAR team only two hours later.

These operations highlighted the difficulties of CSAR where the amount of time and resources committed to the covert rescue of a single pilot seem excessive. At the beginning of the 21st century, AFSOC is attempting to address this problem by preparing for the first of a new generation of special operations aircraft to supplement its existing helicopters - the CV-22 *Osprey*. Bell-Boeing's unique tilt-rotor, multi-mission *Osprey* combines the V/STOL characteristics of helicopter with the dash speed and long range of a conventional fixed-wing aircraft capable of low-visibility, clandestine infiltration/extraction of denied areas in adverse weather

Above: The high-sped low observable (LO) Sikorsky Comanche would make an ideal platform for covert surveillance.

Equipped with a multi-role terrain-following/terrain avoidance (TF/TA) radar and FLIR, cockpit situational awareness during high-speed low-level night flight is enhanced with a head-up Helmet-Mounted Display (HMD) that projects flight symbology over FLIR or NVG imagery. Radar signature-reduction features of the CV-22 include a low-noise, low-flicker prop-rotor system, low-IR paint, low-contrast colour schemes, advanced engine IR suppressers and cockpit electronic emissions control.

US Army rotary wing SOF assets operated by the clandestine 160th Special Operations Aviation Regiment include a fleet of ultra-covert *'Little Bird'* helicopters developed from the Army's Hughes OH-6A *Cayuse* Light Observation Helicopter. Prototypes of the small but nimble *'Little Bird'* were used for covert CIA operations in North Vietnam in the 1970s and attack and utility variants of the more powerful Model 500 *Defender* were later adopted. Fitted with inlet particle filters and IR-suppressing exhausts, and a nose-mounted laser-augmented FLIR, the AH-6J *Nightfox* gunship can be armed with a 7.62 mm Mini-gun, 70 mm rockets and Hellfire anti-tank missiles. Utilised for the insertion/recovery of small SOF teams into denied areas, the MH-6J can carry four fully equipped troops and can be rigged with external pods for SOF assault missions.

Advanced technology rotary-wing aircraft based on the US Army's new generation RAH-66 *Comanche* are likely to replace the *'Little Birds'* in the next decade. Winner of the US Army's Light Helicopter Experimental/Scout Attack (LHX/SCAT) competition, the Boeing Sikorsky RAH-66 *Comanche* involved several 'Black' programmes in developing advanced technology for LHX including the Sikorsky 'X-Wing' Rotor Systems Research Aircraft (RSRA).

Comanche is a Low Observable (LO) armed reconnaissance helicopter designed to replace the US Army's AH-1 *Cobra*, OH-6 and OH-58. The 'stealth' capabilities of the twin-engine two-seat RAH-66 are enhanced by a composite five-shrouded blade bearing-less main rotor, canted fantail anti-torque system, multi-faceted composite fuselage and internal weapons bay. The *Comanche* has an innovative IR suppression system that mixes the exhaust with cool ambient air from inlets in the helicopter's spine. Armed

Above: Canard Rotor Wing (CRW) designs being developed by Boeing will combine vertical take-off/landing with fixed-wing conventional flight.

with Hellfire and Stinger missiles and 20 mm cannon, *Comanche* is designed as a major element of the US Army's future Digital Battlefield. Fitted with digital radios with automatic link establishment software, and advanced data modems, target information and sensor images acquired by *Comanche*'s integrated Target Acquisition System (TAS) and GPS navigator can be transmitted to stand-off 'shooters' in brief digital data-bursts from the safety of a terrain mask, bouncing the Non Line of Sight (NLS) communications off the ionosphere.

Several new hybrid aircraft are also viewed with interest by SOF operators which have the high speed and low RCS of a conventional LO aircraft and the vertical take-off and landing of a helicopter. One of these is the Modus *VertiJet* which has a circular 'disc' wing housing two sets of contra-rotating retractable rotors. With rotor blades fully extended the aircraft takes off vertically like a conventional helicopter and due to the contra-rotating rotors, no anti-torque system is required. Once airborne the landing gear is retracted and the disc hub tilts forward to accelerate the *VertiJet* to a forward speed of nearly 200 mph at which point power to the rotors will be cut and the blades retracted into the disc wing. Two advanced technology turbofans positioned at the roots of an inverted 'V' tailplane, which have combined rudder and elevator control authority, will give the *VertiJet* a maximum speed of over 400 mph.

Boeing's Canard Rotary Wing (CRW) technology, being developed at the Phantom Works, is likely to be introduced into the US Army's RW-X rotorcraft program to replace the SOAR's *Little Birds*. The principle of the CRW is similar to that of the X-wing. The rotor for VTOL operations can be stopped and locked in forward flight to act as a conventional wing at high cruise speed. The exhaust and bypass gasses from its low-bypass turbofan are ducted to nozzles near the rotor/wing tips to maintain rotation and lift. It differs from the X-wing only in that it has a two-blade rotor instead of four. Large foreplanes and a narrow tailplane with canted tips, both fitted with high-lift flaps for take-off and landing, will give the CRW a top speed of 450 mph in conventional fight mode with the stopped rotor acting as a main wing.

The fixed wing element of US and British SOF fleets are mainly derivatives of the ubiquitous C-130 *Hercules*. USAF AC, HC and MC-130s plus RAF *Hercules* C-3s are the backbone of NATO long-range SOF operations, while a small force of USAF C-141 *Starlifters* are dedicated to low-level special operations. Part of the 16th Airlift Squadron (AS) based at Charleston AFB in South Carolina, C-141B SOLL IIs (Special Operations Low-Level II), equipped with chin-mounted FLIR advanced Radar Warning Receivers (RWR), IR-detection systems, chaff/flare dispensers and SATCOM, have NVG-compatible glass cockpits. Meanwhile, most of the C-130 types are likely to be replaced by more of the same, the re-engined, re-winged new generation *Hercules*, the C-130J.

One of the more bizarre attempts to increase the use the C-130's short take-off and landing capability only came to light recently. One of the Pentagon's numerous plans to rescue US hostages being held in Tehran in 1980 was to use of a specially-modified C-130 *Hercules* fitted with rockets front and aft, very much like the manoeuvring thrusters fitted to spacecraft. The plan was that the aircraft would try and land in a small area roughly the size of a football pitch, within the city limits of Tehran. On the approach to the field, rockets at the front of the aircraft would be fired causing the aircraft to virtually stop in mid-air and land in a very short space. Special Forces would then rescue the hostages and bring them aboard the aircraft and once aboard, rockets at the rear of the aircraft would be fired to launch it into a very steep climb. It was an amazing concept and, had it worked, the US would have pulled off one of the most spectacular rescues ever. The project however was never attempted, due to a catastrophic failure of the rocket systems during flight trials, resulting in the destruction of the modified aircraft as it was attempting a landing. It transpired that the rockets fired too soon, causing a severe fire at a critical time and the pilots had no chance of saving the aircraft.

Although a major setback, the US continued to develop other programmes to create an operational capability for STOVL transport aircraft. One name that has been linked with Area 51 is the code-name *Senior Citizen*, a project designed to produce a low-observable (LO), short-take-off and landing (STOL) transport aircraft, for the use of special forces. This could be a derivative of Boeing's No-Tail Advanced Theater Transport (NOTAIL ATT) dubbed *Super Frog*. This was a 'White' programme to produce a tilt-wing transport aircraft similar in size and capacity to the C-130 that would have a STOVL capability, however without a tail. It is believed that this project was developed from a 'Black' programme and possibly the prototype may be revealed in the near future as an SOF platform.

Right: The Boeing C-17A Globemaster III intra-theatre heavy transport in tactical mode firing chaff and flares

Above: One of the Soviet Union's first 'Caspian Sea Monsters' was the 550 tonne ten-engine KM-8 ekranoplan.

At the other end of the scale, Boeing is offering the USAF a variant of the C-17A *Globemaster III* modified for special operations as a potential replacement for the C-141B SOLL II.

It could be that a more likely long-term replacement for both the rotary wing MH-47 *Chinook* and the fixed wing MC-130 *Combat Talon* for night/adverse weather, low-level, deep penetration tactical SOF missions will be hybrid VTOL type designed initially as battlefield tactical transports, as was the C-130, such as the Bell Quad Tiltor (QTR) or the European X-Wing *Titan*. A C-130 size development of the CH-22 *Osprey*, the QTR would be powered by four Rolls-Royce Allison tuboprops and feature 'smart' materials in its construction including composites for low observability (LO). The stealthy *Titan* has been designed to be capable of meeting the US requirement for a new heavy lift VTOL vehicle. They could both carry a very significant defensive/offensive armament, comprising of forward and rearward cannon turrets and AIM-9L or AIM-120 air-to-air missiles.

The *Titan*'s X-wing comprises four rotor blades at 90° to each other with a length x chord of 62 ft x 6 ft. These blades have a bi-convex section to allow them to produce equal lift with either the leading edge or trailing edge facing the oncoming flow. In VTOL mode, the X-wing operates like a conventional helicopter with the blades rotating to provide a relative airflow and hence lift. In forward flight (conventional aircraft mode), the blades are brought to rest at 45° to the longitudinal axis of the craft. In this mode, known as Stop Fold, they form a tandem wing arrangement, with the forward pair of wings swept forward and the rear set of wings swept ‍ft. This configuration combines some of the best features of rotary and fixed wing aircraft. The rotor disc has a large lifting capacity, which enhances its VTOL flight capabilities. In addition to the stopped rotors, the high aspect ratio blades form effective lifting surfaces, which are augmented by the fixed wings at the nose and tail of the fuselage.

In the clandestine world of unconventional warfare in the 21st century, this rapidly expanding number of new generation assets may hold the balance between success and failure in the growing number of out of area (OOA) operations that will be the pattern for future conflicts. Interestingly, some of these harp back to a previous era when flying boats ruled the air, and the sea.

Above: The Russian Navy's *Lun* anti-submarine warfare (ASW) ekranoplan firing a salvo of six cruise missiles.

>>> Water Wings <<<

One of the Soviet Union's most closely guarded secrets during the Cold War was the development of giant 'wingships', the Russian word for which was *ekranoplan*. These hybrid craft were a mix of flying boat and hydrofoil.

The Soviet *ekranoplan*, designed to transport hundreds of troops over long distances at high speeds, was virtually a warship with stub wings that enabled it to 'fly' at up to 50 ft over water on ground or water effect, essentially a cushion of air. The chief designer of these Soviet Wing-in-Ground effect (WIG) programmes, Rostislav Alexiev, exploited this phenomenon to produce some of the largest flying machines ever built. It was not until 1967 that a US spy satellite first revealed the existence of a huge *ekranoplan* docked at a Soviet Naval facility on the shores of the Caspian Sea. Larger than a B-52 and

Above: A medium naval transport ekranoplan, the A-90 is powered by jet lift engines and

Above: A pair of Russian Navy A-90 ekranoplans patrolling the Caspian Sea are capable of speeds of up to 250mph.

Jet', it was promptly christened the 'Caspian Sea Monster'. It was 345 ft long, with a wingspan of 130 ft, weighed 540 tonnes and was powered by ten turbojet engines - eight for take-off and two for cruising a 250 mph. A dozen of these Sea Monsters were operated by the Soviet Navy in the 1970s and a new generation was on the stocks when the Soviet Union imploded and production ground to a halt, although a number of smaller, three-engined A-90 naval transports have continued to be operated spasmodically over the Caspian.

At the end of the Cold War, a successor to the 'Caspian Sea Monsters', the upgraded *Spasatel*, a search and rescue *ekranoplan*, was under construction at the Volga shipbuilding plant. Ten years later it is still waiting to be completed.

Several other WIG projects were attempted in the post-Soviet 1990s but few succeeded beyond the drawing board. It was clear that there would be no substantial funding for many of these projects in Russia and several 'Caspian Sea Monster' designers and engineers moved to California where AeroSea Innovations is currently designing 1,500 tonne cargo-carrying *ekranoplans*. However, the military species is by no means extinct. Lockheed Martin is undertaking low-key research programmes into the potential of small and medium scale WIGs as landing craft and special forces platforms in the future. The American FlareCraft Corporation is also building a series of small stealthy WIG craft, constructed of composite materials and powered by low-powered piston engines. With a range of some 400 miles, the Low Observable (LO) five-place FlareCraft could deliver a small SOF team from the well deck of a Marine assault ship to hostile beaches over the horizon. The US Marine Corps has a requirement for a fast stealthy ground WIG effect craft for special missions and has tested two small FlareCraft Corporation designs.

Australia is now in the forefront of WIG technology thanks to an Australian Defence Acquisition Organisation (DAO) requirement for a new amphibious watercraft for the Australian Defence Forces. One of the companies responding to the DAO requirement is Begul Aviation which is developing the Advanced Air Vehicle (AAV), a twin-hulled semi-rigid airship. Constructed of Kevlar and multi-layer composites that can be coated with Radar Absorbing Material (RAM), the AAV's aerofoil hulls are filled with helium to increase buoyancy in the air and on water and to extend endurance.

Above: The British AVPRO Marauder Wing-in-Ground (WIG) effect concept can be adapted as an Out-of Ground Effect (OGE) conventional aircraft.

A more conventional WIG has been designed by another Australian company. The Queensland-based Flightship FS8, an eight-seat all-composite sea-skimming craft powered by a 450 hp General Motors V8, which gives it a cruising speed of 100 mph and a range of 500 miles, is a proof of concept for a larger watercraft which could carry military vehicles, passengers or equipment weighing up to 50 tonnes.

An innovative British WIG concept, the AVPRO *Marauder*, has been designed as an Out-of-Ground Effect (OGE) craft that can fly as a conventional aircraft. Two basic versions of the stealthy *Marauder* are proposed, one that can 'fly' a few metres above the water surface as a WIG, but in addition, it can be operated out-of-ground effect as a conventional flying boat. The second version operates as a conventional aircraft out-of-ground effect but cannot be operated on the surface of the water as it does not have the hull of the combined-

Above: The WIG variant of the stealthy Marauder can be used as a Special Forces platform for covert operations.

Above: The OGE variant of Marauder may operate as a low-observable strike aircraft in limited 'bush-war' scenarios.

capability version. Both versions of the twin turbofan-powered craft are based on a common airframe of composite construction. The design of the *Marauder* is modular so that it can be reconfigured according to the required role; for example, an anti-submarine warfare (ASW) version equipped with a sea-going hull can be converted to a strike aircraft by replacing the hull with a bomb bay. *Marauder* would also make a highly effective Special Forces landing craft. In addition to two crew, it is intended to carry up to 12 fully equipped troops in a bay inside the hull. The ability of the craft to approach a coastline at low level and high speed would reduce the probability of detection and the exposure of the crew/troops. It would also be capable of making a high speed approach to the drop zone in OGE mode and by cutting the throttles and allowing the craft to glide to touch down in IGE mode hence reduce acoustic signature and making detection by the enemy less risky.

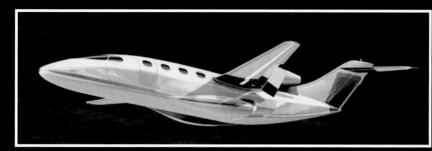

Above: Although developed as a commercial aircraft, the innovative composite-construction Nauticair 450 amphibian would be a cabable SF platform.

Above: The Nauticair 400 combines the high-speed cruise and low-speed handling of a FSW with the water capability of WIG.

The second basic version of the Marauder does not have the hull of the combined capability version and therefore cannot be used as a surface vessel but could be utilised as a conventional escort aircraft acting as a *Sandy* for the OGE SF variant during covert operations. These could be configured for either a close air support mission carrying a range of modern stand-off stores or advanced air-to-air missiles such as the AIM-120 and the proposed FMRAAM allowing it to be used as an interceptor.

Other specialist technology that will be bought to bear in future SOF platforms includes the American Nauticair 450 flying boat. Following trials at the Langley NASA high subsonic wind tunnel in Virginia, designer Dr Gioia developed a sponsored tunnel-hull fuselage which produced unprecedented hydrodynamic stability as well as relatively low drag high-speed aerodynamic performance. It also provides a shallow draft of less than 18 inches making operations in shallow water a possibility.

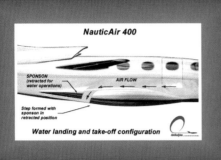

NauticAir 400

SPONSON
(retracted for
water operations)

AIR FLOW

Step formed with
sponson in
retracted position

Water landing and take-off configuration

Above: A tunnel hull and retractable step in the Nauticair's sponsons provide exceptional water take-off performance.

As Dr Gioia began work on a prototype, he teamed up with former Grumman chief engineer Roy LoPresti to develop the Nauticair 450 using his patented hydrodynamic design. Wing floats are not necessary as sponsons with retracting 'steps' and the tunnel hull are designed to provide exceptional water and land take-off performance. The Nauticair also features a Forward Swept Wing (FSW) to give excellent low speed handling combined with a high cruise speed. Mostly constructed of composite materials and powered by two 2,300 lb thrust Williams/Rolls-Royce FJ44-2 turbofans, the Nauticair will cruise at over 500 mph with a range of 1,800 miles. Able to carry up to eight troops, the Nauticair 450 is in the same class as the flying boat version of the *Marauder* for maritime patrol, search and rescue, drug surveillance and Special Forces roles while its designers foresee the development and production of much larger aircraft, even of the C-130 category, utilising their tunnel-hull sponson concept.

The ultimate hybrid SF platform was studied by the US Navy Bureau of Naval Weapons and General Dynamics in the late 1960s. It was the GD Sub-Plane - a flying submarine! Powered by electric motors and batteries, the 10-seat craft would fly to a target area, then dive below the surface to a depth of 75 feet and approach an enemy coastline with the stealth of a submarine. The programme concluded that development of such a vehicle, which could fly up to 500 miles at a speed of 200 mph, with an underwater range of 50 miles at 5 knots, was both feasible and practical. At the time, its cost proved to be prohibitive but with modern technologies and composite construction, does a Sub-Plane exist?

The future of water-borne military aircraft for special missions in the 21st century is full of innovative possibilities although the 'Golden Age' of the flying boat was considered to have ended half a century earlier.

Few countries can afford to develop or acquire dedicated SOF and CSAR assets but one of the most exciting and cost effective pieces of kit that could revolutionise future SOF/CSAR operations is EXINT, an aircraft pod that can be used for the speedy insertion/extraction of Special Forces and recovery of downed aircrew. The UK advanced concept company AVPRO, together with Hunting Engineering and the Defence Evaluation Research Agency (DERA), have developed a low cost solution to this problem by designing the self-contained EXINT (Extraction/Insertion) pod. This pod was originally developed for the UK Armed Forces for special operations and aircrew rescue using the V/STOL capabilities of the BAe *Harrier/Sea Harrier*, and the WAH-64D *Apache* attack helicopter.

The concept can trace its origins back to World War Two when both Britain and Germany developed a series of man-carrying pods to be carried by operational aircraft. The most successful were designed for use by the *Luftwaffe's* famed KG 200, which operated a mixed fleet of more than 50 aircraft including captured B-17 and B-24 bombers for dropping secret agent into western Europe, the Soviet Union and the Middle East.

Developed by the *Forschungsanstalt Graf Zeppelin* at Stuttgart, two-man lightweight gondolas were fitted above the wings of Klemm 35 trainers and later Ju87D *Stukas*. They were released in a shallow dive to descend by parachute to deliver secret agents. Similar pods were fitted to Fw190 fighters under an experimental programme code-named *Doppelreiter* (Double-rider), but there is no record of any of these pods being used operationally.

Right: Royal Navy Barracuda torpedo-bombers were fitted with man-carrying under-wing panniers during World War Two.

Below: The concept has been bought into the 21st century by the AVPRO EXINT pod here carried under the wing of a Harrier II.

Above: The under-wing EXINT pod can be used for the carriage of aircrew, Special Forces, equipment or flight spares.

The RAF had flown agents into neutral Sweden in the bomb bays of *Mosquito* fighter-bombers while a *Barracuda* torpedo-bomber carrying two two-man under-wing pods took part in trials at the Airborne Forces Experimental Establishment at Beaulieu. The paratroopers would be ejected through a trap door in the floor, hopefully, having been warned beforehand by the pilot.

Since then, the concept has been considerably refined by the designers of EXINT and as the project developed it has become apparent that the pod would fit all NATO attack helicopters including non-western designs, thus giving every NATO air force a SOF/CSAR capability using existing assets. When not being utilised for personnel carrying roles, the EXINT pod can be used for the carriage of equipment, ground crew, and flight spares. This capability is of great significance in out-of-area (OOA) operations as it enables attack helicopter units to self-deploy without the need for support helicopters, making tactical operations more flexible and efficient.

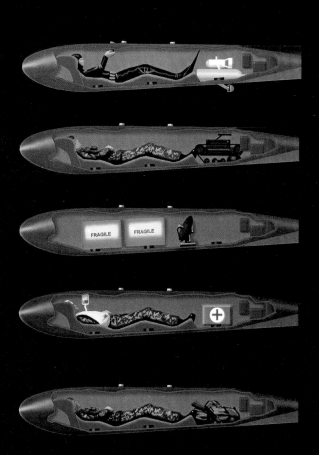

Above: Some of the many roles of the EXINT pod include Special Forces insertion, forward equipment carriage, medivac and ground crew transport.

Above: One of the many front-line combat types able to carry EXINT pods includes the RAF Jaguar strike aircraft.

121

Above: One of the first combat aircraft to be deployed with EXINT is the British Army's new WAH-64D Apache now entering service.

In the light of US forces' experience in Kosovo, where huge amounts of valuable helicopter assets were tied up with supporting Army *Apache* units, considerable interest is being shown in EXINT. The USMC is looking to deploy EXINT for use on its *Cobra* attack helicopters and VSTOL AV-8B *Harrier* aircraft. As one senior member of the USMC recently stated: "EXINT is a neat tool and we want it for our guys". In addition to the UK and USA, 18 other countries have made formal approaches to purchase the system.

EXINT is a one-man pod of some 12 ft in length, fitted with radio, GPS and air conditioning systems. An equipment bay also allows small arms and other personal equipment to be carried. A state-of-the-art parachute and airbag system, developed from the Marslander Spacecraft programme will allow the pod to make a soft landing should it be released from the aircraft in an emergency situation. The other main feature of EXINT, which is of particular interest to the Special Forces, is its ability to float on water, and a small electric motor for propulsion can be fitted if required. James Bond's 'Q' would have loved it.

Above: The EXINT pod is currently being flight-tested on the VSTOL Harrier II used

Above: Future carriers of the EXINT pod may include the Boeing F-32B ASTOVL Joint Strike Fighter (JSF).

Above: Another is the US Army's latest low-observable armed reconnaissance helicopter, the RAH-66 Comanche.

Above: The world's first variable geometry (VG) jet fighter was the Messerschmitt P.1101 captured by the Allies in 1945 before it flew.

>>> Swing Wing <<<

In the 1960s the answer to high-speed military aviation seemed to be variable geometry (VG), or the 'swing-wing'. Designers argued that VG was the perfect compromise that gave supersonic dash speed with fully swept wings combined with excellent handling at low speeds with wings extended.

The most obvious application of VG was for high performance carrier-borne aircraft and the Grumman XF10F-1 *Jaguar* was designed in 1948 to demonstrate the system's capabilities to the US Navy. The concept, however, had already been researched by Willy Messerschmitt in 1944. The jet-powered VG P.1101 was 75% complete when the Allied Air Technical Intelligence Team discovered it at Oberammergau in April 1945. It was transported to the Bell factory at Buffalo, New York, along with Messerschmitt's chief aerodynamist, Joseph Hubert, who was 'recruited' by the USA as part of Operation *Paperclip*. The VG Bell X-5, which made its first flight in June 1951, was based on the P.1101 and offered to USAF as a prototype Mach 1.0 interceptor. But as with the Grumman *Jaguar*, the X-5 suffered from handling difficulties and a lack of range and weapons capacity due to overweight and showed no advantage over conventional designs.

Above: Inspired by the Me P.1101 was the US Bell X-5 VG fighter prototype which flew for the first time in June 1951.

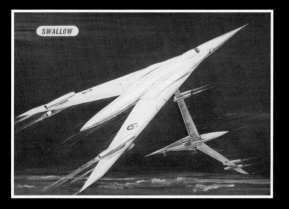

SWALLOW

Above: British designer Barnes Wallis researched the VG concept with models of his tailless supersonic Swallow.

Coincidentally, the chief designer of a British Vickers/Royal Aircraft Establishment (RAE) transonic programme, Barnes Wallis, was researching a variable wing sweep configuration code-named *Wild Goose*. Designed to be powered by a hydrogen peroxide fuelled 'cold motor', experimental half-scale vehicles of the tailless arrowhead concept, code-named *Heyday*, which featured a wing pivoted at mid-point, were tested in water tanks at the National Physical Laboratory at Teddington, but were unsuccessful. Wallis adapted the design into a highly-swept arrowhead, known as the *Swallow*, with VG wings pivoted at the shoulders. Supersonic flights of model *Swallow* took place at rocket ranges in

Above: The first successful operational VG combat aircraft was the Mach 2.0 General Dynamics F-111
which served with USAF for more than three decades.

England and Wales, some of which reached Mach 2.5 before the project was cancelled in 1957 along with most of Britain's supersonic manned aircraft projects.

Some of Wallis's staff were transferred to the USA to continue their work with Grumman and General Dynamics who were about to pick up the VG baton where it was dropped by the XF10F and X-5 a decade earlier. The result was the first operational VG, the F-111 Mach 2.0 two-seat fighter-bomber developed for a single USAF/USN programme known as Tactical Fighter Experiment (TFX). Exhaustive wing-tunnel tests at the NASA Langley facility had established that, given the correct wing-taper and tailplane position, the variable-geometry wing was more efficient than a conventional swept-wing design. But there were penalties. Nevertheless, more than 400 F-111s were built for the USAF, the first of which entered service in 1967, many serving with distinction for over three decades in Vietnam, the Gulf War and the Balkans, and they will continue to be operated well into the 21st century by the Royal Australian Air Force.

The shipboard version, the F-111B, to be built by Grumman, was abandoned in 1968. Grumman, however, had been convinced that VG was the answer to operating high-performance combat aircraft from aircraft carriers and despite the setback experienced with the XF10F programme, devoted another ten years to overcome the problems.

Four years later, President Reagan revived the project and ordered 100 improved versions into production. The B-1B *Lancer* took advantage of recent 'stealth' technology such as reprofiled engine intakes, composite components and the application of Radar Absorbing Material (RAM), but service trials were long and costly. After entering service with Strategic Air Command (SAC) in 1985, the transition to the low-level proved difficult for the B-1B and several were lost. With the end of the Cold War, its role was diminished. It was held back from operations during the Gulf War and was not committed into action until Operation *Desert Fox*, the return match over Iraq nearly 14 years after it entered service.

The variable-geometry craze was also in full swing on the other side of the Iron Curtain in the 1960s. Mikoyan developed a series of supersonic VG fighters starting with the MiG-23 *Flogger-A* in 1967 which featured a full wing sweep similar to the F-111. The Sukhoi bureau's first into the 'swing-wing' era was the Su-17 *Fitter-B*, based on the earlier Su-7 fitted with pivoted outer wings. Its most capable VG attack aircraft was the two-seat Su-24 *Fencer*, which saw action in Afghanistan and Chechnya and was exported to Iraq, Iran, Libya and Syria in the 1980s. However, one of the few Soviet long-range bombers that caused considerable concern in the West was the product of the Tupolev bureau. The Mach 2.0 long-range VG Tu-22M *Backfire* strategic bomber entered service with Soviet Long Range Aviation units in the early 1970s. Slightly smaller than the B-1B but with better performance, the *Backfire* is still in production.

The Tu-22M's big brother, the *Blackjack*, originally seen as a B-1B copy, was first revealed to the West in 1981. The Tu-160 was in fact the heaviest and most powerful combat aircraft ever to fly and was launched to counter the B-1 threat, regardless of cost. With an unrefuelled range of 6,000 miles and a sea level speed of Mach 1.0, only a small number of the Soviet's 'billion rouble bombers' had been produced when the Iron Curtain fell and few have remained operational.

The Soviet Union had a number of swing-wing supersonic bomber projects on the stocks at the end of the Cold War,

Above: Often referred to as a Soviet F-111 'copy', the multi-role Sukhoi Su-24 *Fencer* differs in many respects and remains in Russian service.

the most advanced of these from the Myasishchyev bureau. Several variants of the M-20 were designed with different VG wing configurations including four- and six-engined versions, with canard foreplanes, 'T'-tails or droop-wings, but none progressed further than the drawing board.

A stealthy air-refuellable VG Sukhoi T-60S has been designed as a replacement for the *Backfire*, powered by twin high bypass-ratio turbofans with two-dimensional thrust vectoring which would give it high-altitude supersonic cruise of Mach 2.0. Although the Russian Air force has no funds for its Long Range Aviation force, its new government's recent opposition to an expanding and offensive NATO may well change this position in the future.

Above: The heaviest and most powerful combat aircraft ever to enter service, development of the Tu-160 *Blackjack* VG long-range strategic bomber helped to bankrupt the soviet union.

Right: An adaption of a fixed swept-wing fighter, the Soviet VG Su-22M *Fitter* became WarPac's standard strike aircraft in the 1980s.

Below: One of Western Europe's more successful colaborative ventures was the VG Panavia Tornado IDS which serves with the RAF, *Luftwaffe* and the Italian and Saudi Air Forces.

One of Western Europe's most successful combat aircraft of the last two decades is the multi-national VG Panavia *Tornado*. After several abortive European 'swing-wing' programmes of the 1960s, including the Anglo-French Variable Geometry (AFVG) multi-role fighter and the US-German Advanced VSTOL Strike (AVS) fighter, the UK, Germany and Italy finally got their act together to build the Mach 2.0 Panavia Multi-Role Combat Aircraft (MCRA). Known in service as the *Tornado* Interdictor/Strike (IDS), the first of almost 1,000 production examples flew in 1978. Its first operational missions were flown in Operation *Desert Storm* during which six RAF *Tornado* GR.1s were lost making a series of low-level attacks on Iraqi airfields using JP233 airfield denial weapons. They were subsequently used in Operation *Desert Fox* while German ECM *Tornadoes* became the first *Luftwaffe* aircraft to undertake combat missions since 1945 when they took part in Operation *Allied Force* over Kosovo 55 years later.

Less successful was the *Tornado* Air Defence Variant (ADV), a long-range bomber interceptor development of the two-seat *Tornado* IDS which was adopted by the RAF and the Royal Saudi Air Force. Soon after it entered service in the late 1980s, its role ceased to exist and the RAF was left without an agile air defence/air superiority fighter for the next decade.

Left: Designed as a long-range bomber killer during the Cold War, the RAF swing-wing Tornado F.3 is no dog-fighter and will soon be replaced by the Eurofighter Typhoon.

However, by then, the 'swing-wing' fashion was on the wane. No new variable-geometry fourth or fifth generation combat aircraft were designed in the 1990s. Even the Soviet Union's MiG-29 *Fulcrum* and Su-27 *Flanker* were conventional aircraft using fly-by-wire flight control systems to enhance low-speed handling and manoeuvrability.

In the West, close-coupled canards, which were pioneered by Saab with its potent *Viggin* in the late 1970s, are the latest 'in-fashion' for 21st century fighters such as the F-22 *Raptor*, Eurofighter *Typhoon*, Dassault *Rafale* and Saab *Gripen*. Add to this thrust-vectoring and supercruise and the 'swing-wing' concept looks dead in the air.

Variable-geometry solved a number of high-performance aircraft problems, but there was a price to pay. Added weight and complexity added up to extra costs. The 'swing-era' is over.

Above: Designed to replace the Russian *Backfire* and *Blackjack* strategic bombers, the swing-wing Sukhoi T-60 will remain a future concept.

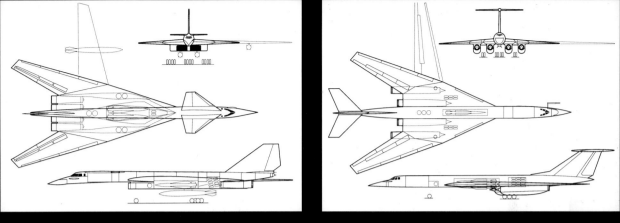

Above: More swing-wing variations on the Russian M-20 long-range straegic bomber that will never leave the drawing boards.

>>> Fast Forward <<<

Ever since the end of the Cold War, the technological capability of Russia's haemorrhaging aerospace industry was considered by the West to be in terminal dive, but that all changed 19 days after the much-vaunted Lockheed Martin F-22 Raptor made it first flight on 7 September 1997. On 25 September, Sukhoi's chief test-pilot Igor Votintsev flew the company's S-37 *Berkut* (Royal Eagle) in complete secrecy from the LI Institute flight test centre at Zhukovskii near Moscow. Catching Western observers by surprise, the appearance of the S-37, a 'fifth generation' fighter project, was for Russia the most important aerospace event of the decade.

Developed in response to a 1981 Soviet requirement for fighters for the 1990s, Sukhoi commenced designing an advanced, heavy-fighter concept in 1983 known as the S-32, in competition with Mikoyan which submitted its Product 1.42. The unique aspect of the Sukhoi S-32 was that it featured a forward-swept wing (FSW) which the authorities decided was too radical and the more conventional 1.42 won government funding. In the event, this virtually dried up after the Soviet Union imploded and although production of a 1.42 prototype, known as the 1.44, began, it lost the race to be Russia's first 'fifth generation' fighter to fly. In the meantime, development of Sukhoi's S-32 continued under cover, with meagre government funding supplemented by export sales of the company's successful Su-27 *Flanker* family of heavyweight combat aircraft.

There had long been rumours of the existence of these two aircraft; in fact the 1.44 was virtually complete five years before its first flight in March 2000. Models of the S-32 had been shown at trade shows but few observers realised how far the project, later re-designated S-37, had progressed before its first flight in 1997.

The concept of FSW was not new. It can be traced back to 1943 German designs. The Junkers Ju 287 was a jet-powered heavy bomber with a forward-swept wing designed to outrun Allied fighter aircraft and, at the same time, have excellent low-speed handling. A prototype, with four temperamental Jumo 004B turbojets supplemented by four jettisonable Walter 501 auxiliary rocket motors to assist take-off, made its maiden flight on 16 August 1944. Designed to have a top speed of 625 mph and a range of 1,000 miles, production of the Ju 287, along with all bomber aircraft, was cancelled soon after the prototype's first flight.

Low scale development on a second aircraft continued in secret until the German Air Ministry belatedly placed orders for 100 production aircraft per month - in March 1945. A month later, Soviet troops overran the Junkers plant at Dessau in East Germany and the second prototype was transported to the Soviet Union along with its designer Dr Hans Wocke and his team of technicians. These German 'guest workers' were housed in a secure complex,' known as OKB-1, at Podberezye, some 100 miles east of Moscow. Here work continued on the second Ju 287, which made a number of test flights before the project was terminated at the end of 1947. By this time, a new improved version, the six-engined EF 131, was under construction and later flight-tested at LI Institute at Zhukovskii. Development was cancelled in 1949.

Above: Designed as a long-range jet-bomber at the end of World War Two was the forward-swept wing (FSW) Junkers 287 that was later flight tested in the Soviet Union.

Above: A new shape flies from Zhukovskii - Russia's FSW Sukhoi S-37 *Berkut* which surprised the West when it first flew in 1997.

Above: One of NASA's most successful research aircraft was the Grumman X-29A used to prove that the FSW concept improved manoeuvrability and low-speed handling.

Although the FSW concept proved to be successful at both high and low-speed, conventionally constructed metal wings were prone to warping and required considerable strengthening, which in turn added weight and reduced performance.

Another German FSW project that progressed no further than the concept phase was the Blohm und Voss P209.02 single-seat jet fighter, which inspired a number of projects in both the United States and Soviet Union. The Tsybin OKB produced a FSW version of a transonic glider, the LL-3 which made more than 100 flights at Zhukovskii during the late 1940s. American designs that got no further than the drawing board included the Convair XB-53 jet bomber project of 1945 which made use of German FSW research as did a Douglas D-558-1 *Skystreak* with FSW which was a joint US Navy/NACA program.

An FSW version of the rocket-powered Bell X-1, the first aircraft to break the sound barrier in level flight, was wind tunnel-tested by NASA in 1948. Wing warping continued to be a major problem with all of these projects and it would be more than 30 years before another successful FSW jet fighter would take to the air.

Responding to a Defense Advanced Research Projects Agency (DARPA) requirement for a highly manoeuvrable transonic aircraft with low-speed controllability and low stalling and landing speeds, Grumman developed the X-29A as it was officially designated by the USAF, using the forward fuselage of a Northrop F-5A, fitted with a carbon fibre wing and fin, and large canard foreplanes which replaced a tailplane. The driving force behind this project was the use of new technology advanced composite materials. Powered by 16,000lb thrust GE F404 after-burning turbofan which gave it maximum speed of Mach 1.6, the Grumman X-29A made its maiden flight from Edwards AFB, California, on 14 December 1984. To avoid the wings twisting during sustained high-'g' turns, the carbon-fibre plies

Above: A Royal Navy Future Carrier-Borne Aircraft (FCBA) concept of a highly-agile FSW design which could be a CTOL or ASTOVL multi-role platform.

used in the manufacture of the wing skins can be used to make the wing twist in a controlled way as it bends.

The first X-29A flew a total of 254 missions without mishap over a period of four years while the second FSW aircraft flew another 120 between 23 May 1989 and October 1991. The X-29 programme proved that an FSW concept had a lower drag throughout the entire operational envelope although it was particularly significant at transonic speeds where a reduction of up to 20% could be achieved. Control response was also excellent at up to 45% angle of attack (AoA) while other advantages included improved manoeuvrability, and virtual spin-proof characteristics.

In 1985 Grumman submitted an FSW design based on the X-29A for the USAF Advanced Tactical Fighter (ATF) competition which was eventually won by the F-22 in 1991. As far as the United States was concerned, there was no future for FSW combat aircraft. However, a year before the X-29A first flew, Sukhoi had flown an experimental FSW aircraft. Initially spotted by a US intelligence satellite at Saki airfield, close to Syberski in the Black Sea region, the Sukhoi FSW was code-named SYB-A, in the tradition of indexing Soviet experimental aircraft according to the places there were first seen. What was interesting was that the SBY-A was also seen at one of the Soviet Navy's air bases which may give a clue to the genesis of the S-32/7.

At the time, the Soviet Navy was planning to construct four large 'blue water' aircraft carriers and with its short take-off run, excellent low-speed handling and super-manoeuvrability, the *Berkut* would make an ideal and highly capable carrier-borne combat aircraft. In the event, only one Soviet carrier was completed, the *Admiral Kuznetsov*, one virtually completed and later sold to the Indian Navy, a third scrapped on the slipway and the

fourth cancelled. Ironically, when the
Kuznetsov was first deployed by the Russian
Navy in 1996, its complement included a
squadron of navalised *Flankers*, the Su-27K
which was fitted with canard foreplanes, a
strengthened landing gear, folding wings and
a shortened tailcone.

The S-37, initially powered by two 30,000
lb thrust Lyulka-Saturn AL-31F after-burning
turbofans as fitted to the Su-27, is very
much larger than the X-29, 74 ft long with a
wingspan of nearly 55 ft; it also had twin
fins and all-moving tailplanes. When fitted
with 40,000 lb thrust Saturn AL-41F low-
bypass after- burning turbofans, the S-37's
maximum design speed will be Mach 2.0 with a
supercruise speed of over 1,000 mph and a
subsonic unrefuelled range of 2,500 miles.

Although the S-37 has a large internal
armaments bay, it is still a concept
demonstrator rather than a fighter prototype.
After flying more than 60 test flights in

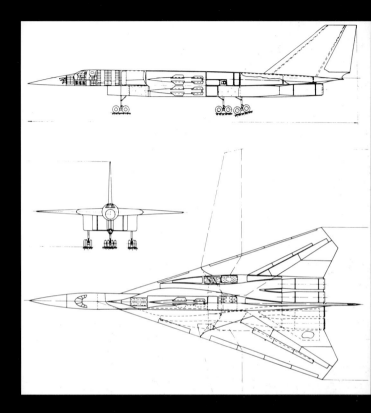

Above: A hang-over from the Cold War, this is one of many swing-wing Soviet strategic bomber variants of the proposed Myasishchyev M-20.

three years, it has yet to be fitted with operational radar, avionics, weapons systems, or thrust-vector control (TVC), but does have a full triplex digital fly-by-wire (FBW) control system. However, these will obviously be influenced by equipment being developed for the latest export variants of the *Flanker* family.

Typically in the past, Russian aerospace design has put less emphasis on stealth than its American counterparts and with large canard foreplanes and all-moving tailplanes, its radar cross section (RCS) will be greater than its western counterparts. On the plus side are an internal weapons bay, shielded engine ducts and some use of Radar Absorbing Material (RAM) and paint, and the prospect of refining a plasma radar-blocking device being developed by Moscow's M V Keldysh Research Centre.

Coincidentally, during the development of the S-37, the UK DERA was evaluating a design study of an FSW concept by the British company AVPRO as a contender for the Royal Air Force's Future Offensive Air System (FOAS) programme. This confirmed all the positive aspects of FSW that both the X-29 and S-37 programmes had experienced. However AVPRO studied several additional design features, such as all-moving wingtips, V-type inlet ducts and a gull-wing, that improved performance and the platform's RCS. At supersonic speeds, the all-moving wingtips would provide far superior roll control to trailing edge devices and this along with the large moment arm was the main reason for using them. When the aircraft is flying at supersonic speed the wingtips influence the flow over the whole area of the wingtips. By contrast, trailing edge devices only influence the flowfield downstream of the hingeline.

Above: The Rapier, an AVPRO concept of a future RAF Forward Swept Wing (FSW) agile fighter.

Above: AVPRO's concept for the Royal Navy's Future Carrier-Borne Aircraft (FCBA)

'Doodlebugs' to 'Robobugs'

The concept of the remotely piloted aircraft stretches back even further than manned aircraft. Aviators' first experiments into flight comprised mainly model aircraft built to resemble birds or flying insects. Few were successful until the invention of the internal combustion engine, following which manned and unmanned aircraft were developed in parallel.

One of the first 'Black' programmes in World War One was the invention of the automatic gyroscopic stabiliser by Americans Dr Peter Cooper and Elmer A Sperry, who carried out experiments using converted US Navy Curtiss N-9 biplane trainers powered by a 40 hp engine carrying a 300 lb bomb load as 'aerial torpedoes' in 1918. A more sophisticated version, known as the 'Kettering Bug', was built in large quantities by General Motors but never used operationally.

The breakthrough in unmanned aircraft technology came in the Second World War with Germany's first secret weapon, the Fiesler Fi-103 'flying bomb', better known as the V-1 'Revenge Weapon'. Project *Kirschkern* (Cherry Stone) was the codename for the pulse-jet-powered unmanned aircraft carrying a 2,000 lb warhead designed to be launched from a 250 ft-long ramp, cruise at 400 mph and be pre-programmed to fly between 100-150 miles before its engine cut out and it dropped on its target. Nearly 6,000 V-1s fell on British cities, where it was christened the 'Doodlebug', between June 1944 and January 1945, killing more than 900 people, mainly civilians.

The highly advanced V-1 was used to develop the United States' post-war missile and UAV programmes, the most successful of which was the Ryan *Firebee* family. Designed originally as a unmanned target drone, the *Firebee* was developed into a family of high and low-altitude surveillance and electronic intelligence (ELINT) UAVs during the Vietnam war. The *Firebee* also became the first Unmanned Combat Air Vehicle (UCAV) under another 'Black' programme of the mid-1970s.

Above: One of the first, and most successful Unmanned Aerial Vehicles (UAV) were the multi-role Ryan Firebee family used the American Services for nearly three decades.

Fitted with a laser designator and TV cameras in the nose, *Pathfinder* was capable of acquiring targets for a variety of air-to-ground weapons ranging from Mk 82 iron bombs to *Maverick* air-to-ground missiles (AGM). Guided by operators in its 'mother' DC-130 *Hercules* launch aircraft, *Pathfinder* could not only find its targets but hit them with some accuracy. However the end of the war in Vietnam also spelt the end of the *Firebee* bomber programme.

Other 'Black' unmanned programmes that were spawned by the South East Asia conflicts were the air-launched Mach 3 D-21 Project *Tagboard*, which suffered from being in front of then

Above: After World War Two, the United States developed a series of UAVs from the German pulse-jet powered 'Revenge Weapon - the V-1 'Doodlebug'.

known technology, and the ultra secret Teledyne Ryan Model 154 *Compass Arrow*, the first high-altitude reconnaissance UAV to have contoured structural shapes that shadowed engine intakes and exhaust ducts and was covered in a Radar Absorbing Material (RAM) coating to minimise its RCS. Stealth had been discovered.

Throughout the 1970s and 1980s, a series of successful short-range piston-engined tactical reconnaissance UAVs with limited sensor payloads were produced by Israel, some of which were used by the US Marine Corps in the Gulf and Balkan wars. But it was the Defense Advanced Research Projects Agency's (DARPA) *Tier* program that would push known UAV technologies to their practical limits. Developed from a CIA 'Black' programme UAV, the General Atomics Gnat 750, the first of the USAF's 'dream team' of high-tech Unmanned Reconnaissance Air Vehicles (URAV) was the General Atomics RQ-1A *Predator*. Officially known as Tier II Medium-Altitude Endurance (MAE) UAV, *Predator* first flew in 1995 and a year later was flown operationally over Bosnia by a detachment of the USAF's 11th Reconnaissance Squadron (RS) based at Indian Springs in the Nellis AFB complex in the Nevada Desert supporting IFOR.

Above: The Vietnam conflict spawned the CIA's D-21 Project *Tagboard* , a Mach 3.0 UAV air-launched from the back of a Lockheed A-12 'mother' ship.

Although the *Predator* is a conventional design built largely of composite materials and powered by a 44 hp pusher piston engine, it has an endurance of 40 hours at a cruising altitude of 25,000 ft carrying a 450 lb sensor payload. Its operations were expanded during Operation *Allied Force* but at least one USAF RQ-1A was shot down by Serb ground fire in Kosovo.

Its larger cousin, the Teledyne Ryan RQ-4A *Global Hawk*, or Tier II Plus High-Altitude Endurance (HAE) surveillance UAV, is powered by the 'low

Above: USAF's only currently operational surveillance UAV is the Predator which was developed from the CIA's Gnat 750 in the mid-1990s.

Above: The half-scale Highly Maneuverable Aircraft Technology (HiMAT) demonstrator was a UAV built by Rockwell to research the limits of future combat aircraft's agility.

burn' 7,050 lb st Rolls-Royce Allison turbofan. The performance of this large UAV, with its wingspan of 116 ft, is impressive. It can remain airborne for more than 40 hours, cruise at 375 mph at 65,000 ft and has a maximum range of 14,500 miles. Its 2,000 lb payload comprises Electro Optical (EO), Infra-Red (IR), Synthetic Aperture Radar (SAR) sensors, active and passive Electronic Support Measures (ESM), on-board data storage and real-time transmission.

While advanced technology will undoubtedly produce fail-safe UAVs in the very near future, sceptics will always point to the inherent dangers of unmanned, which equals uncontrolled, flight. In May 1999, the designer's worst nightmares became reality when the second prototype RQ-4A went out of control at 40,000

Above: USAF Predator UAVs operated from Hungarian fighter bases during the recent Balkan conflicts, two of which were shot down.

Above: Resembling a blind insect, the all-seeing Global Hawk is a high-altitude long-endurance unmanned reconnassance aerial vehicle (URAV).

ft and crashed on the NAWC China Lake's Echo Range near Edwards AFB.

   Three years earlier, the first, and most unconventional design of the three *Tier* project UAVs, the Lockheed Martin/Boeing *DarkStar* Tier III Minus, crashed on its second test flight. The futuristic stealthy flying wing *DarkStar*, powered by the Williams FJ-44 turbofan, was designed to loiter unseen over a battlefield for up to eight hours. A product of the Skunk Works, *DarkStar* first flew in March 1996, but due to software problems that caused the prototype to crash a few weeks later, and rising costs, the project was cancelled soon after a second *DarkStar* flew in 1998. However, it is unlikely that the technology, and expenditure, will be wasted.

Above: Soon to join the USAF's fleet of advanced URAVs, the 116ft wingspan Global Hawk can remain on station for more than 40 hours.

Above: Flying saucers have become a reality with Sikorsky's Cyper II, a tactical vertical take-off/landing URAV known as 'Dragon Warrior' being evaluated by the US Marine Corps.

For the Area 51 'Groomers' there are a number of UAV projects that will send them into ecstasy - they will have seen a UFO! Canadair's CL-227 *Sentinel*, a 6 ft-high VTOL craft designed for the US Navy to be launched and recovered from a warship's helipad, is nicknamed the 'Peanut'. When airborne, its high-revolution contra-rotating rotors cannot be seen and the UAV looks exactly like a flying peanut.

Above: Another science-fiction image is the Canadair CL-227 Sentinel, a ship-borne URAV nicknamed the 'Peanut'.

A real flying saucer called 'Dragon Warrior' has been ordered by the Marine Corps to provide a flexible unmanned surveillance platform. The 7 ft-diameter Sikorsky *Cypher II* can hover like a helicopter, using classified shrouded rotor technology, or, fitted with removable wings, fly like a fixed-wing aircraft at speeds of up to 125 mph over a range of 100 miles.

A similar design concept will be adopted for the British Army's Future Mobile Direct Fire Equipment Requirement (MODIFIER) to replace its Challenger Main Battle Tank (MDT). Its future offensive ground vehicles will each carry their own VTOL 'flying saucer' UAV for battlefield reconnaissance and target acquisition. Seeing is believing!

Above: The first Unmanned Combat Aerial Vehicle (UCAV), the Ryan BGM-34B that successfully test-fired a range of air-launched weapons in the 1970s.

Left: Lockheed Martin's concept of future air warfare includes unmanned variants of the F-16 Fighting Falcon and tailless flying-wing UCAVs.

Left: Tail standing UCAVs with folding wings could operate from small US Navy UAV carriers tasked with fleet protection and surveillance.

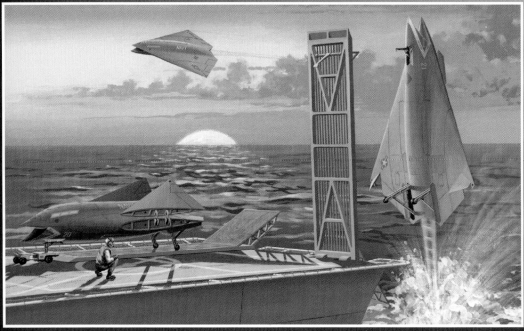

Right: The costly low-level airfield attack missions could be one of the UCAV's primary roles in the future.

>>> UCAV <<<

The next and more controversial step in UAV development is the Unmanned Combat Air Vehicle (UCAV). Many countries, and the United States in particular, find unacceptable the loss of operational aircrew in the 'bush' wars and internal conflicts that have broken out all over the world since the end of the Cold War. The UCAV is therefore seen as the ideal solution to perform 'dull, dirty and dangerous' missions. In an age of declining defence budgets, increasing operational requirements and the continuing development of technology, the UCAV is intended to provide a relatively cheap weapon system capable of carrying out high-risk missions.

Suppression of Enemy Air Defence (SEAD) strikes, Close Air Support (CAS) and armed reconnaissance are the roles usually associated with UCAVs. However, by making use of the advances in computer power, artificial intelligence, virtual reality and jamming resistant data-links, many more interesting roles for these vehicles are possible. The vehicle could operate autonomously as an interceptor, escort for tankers and AWACS/ASTOR, as well as a bomber flying pre-programmed missions but with the ability to deviate from the planned mission to evade enemy defences or to actively engage enemy aircraft.

Another scenario is to assign UCAVs to manned aircraft to act as flying weapons dumps. When the manned aircraft has used all its weapons, it can assign targets to the UCAV and authorise weapon release. Both the manned and unmanned elements of the strike package could communicate with each other via data-links to provide pilots and out-of-theatre commanders with a more complete picture of the tactical situation than could otherwise be achieved. Missions that could not be flown by the on-board computer, such as close-range dogfights, could be flown remotely by a human operator or virtual pilot in a command post, either airborne AWACS, ASTOR or JSTARS aircraft, or in a remote ground station. Data from the onboard sensors such as radar, electro-optical and air-data systems would be transmitted back to the command post and displayed on conventional displays or possibly using a virtual reality (VR) style helmet which would allow the pilot to more easily

Above: Small stealthy and expendable UAVs colud be launched from US Navy submarines for surveillance, target acquisition and communications.

Above: *A stealthy flying-wing UCAV with provision for in-flight refuelling offered by Lockheed Martin for the RAF FOAS programme.*

direct the sensors on the vehicle. The pilot could then engage the enemy aircraft without the physiological problems generated by high 'g' manoeuvres in manned aircraft. This gives the UCAV a tactical advantage in dogfights since it is not restricted by the physiological limits of the pilot and it can easily be designed to be capable of much larger manoeuvre load factors than manned aircraft.

Provision will be made for in-flight refuelling which could be carried out automatically or by a human pilot via remote control. If the vehicle was programmed to fly a Combat Air Patrol (CAP) mission and it had not encountered any hostile aircraft by the time its fuel was running low, it could return to a tanker, air refuel and then fly back to its CAP Station.

The concept was first explored by NASA's Highly Manoeuvrable Aircraft Technology (HiMAT) demonstrator in the early 1980s. HiMAT was a sub-scale research vehicle built by Rockwell to explore the outer limits of

Above: The RAF's concept of the future aerial battlefield includes both manned and umanned strike platforms multi-role stand-off weapons.

manoeuvrability which no pilot could withstand. Carried aloft by a B-52, the HiMATs, two of which were built, demonstrated twice the manoeuvrability of current and projected manned combat aircraft and that they would have been almost impossible to shoot down in air-to-air combat.

The UCAV can also be a maritime-based asset capable of performing air-to-air, air-to-surface and air-to-ground attack as well as reconnaissance missions. As it is more likely to be operated from aircraft carriers, the design of the vehicle would exploit the rolling take-off and landing capability made possible by the flight deck of these vessels.

Lockheed Martin's Skunk Works is studying the possibility of launching UCAVs from submerged submarines in much the same way as *Trident* ballistic missiles. After their mission, they could be recovered by parachute, or trapped in nets on a ship's deck.

An interim proposal that could be used to prove advanced UCAV technologies has also come from Lockheed Martin which plans to convert some of the USAF's many surplus F-16s to an unarmed attack aircraft. BAe Systems has a

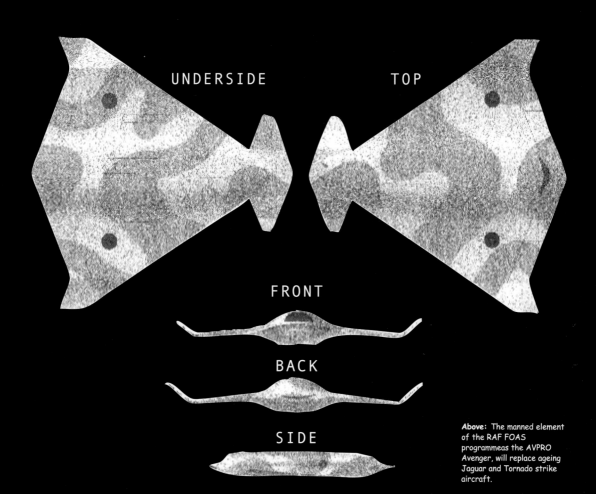

UNDERSIDE   TOP

FRONT

BACK

SIDE

Above: The manned element of the RAF FOAS programmeas the AVPRO Avenger, will replace ageing Jaguar and Tornado strike aircraft.

similar plan to develop unmanned versions of the *Tornado* variable-geometry strike/attack aircraft for RAF's Future Offensive Air System (FOAS) requirement. But it is behind the walls of Boeing's Phantom Works that the DARPA UCAV programme will be developed to demonstrate the technical feasibility and tactical practicality of future UCAVs. At the same time BAe Systems is developing a multinational technology demonstrator at its Special Projects site at Warton to allow evaluation of manned and unmanned technologies, some of which may have already flown. For the past few years there have been several eyewitness reports of a small triangular craft approximately 30 ft-long powered by an exotic propulsion system based on microwave induction which creates shockwaves on which the craft rides.

It is known that the UK's Defence Evaluation and Research Agency (DERA) is working in collaboration with BAe Systems and Clay Research Ltd on an unmanned generic stealth concept and it may be one of these that has been seen flying from Warton, usually escorted by two RAF *Tornadoes* that are used to mask its radar return. DERA is also involved in the development of a much smaller delta-wing URAV called the *Observer*, which will cruise around a local battlefield area at 1,000 ft downloading data to an infantry battalion HQ. It would be designed to be so simple that "even a brigadier could operate it."

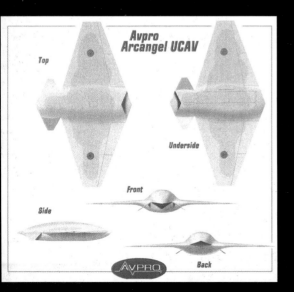

Above and Below: Designed to fly the 'dull, dirty and dangerous' missions, UCAVs such as the AVPRO Arcangel will be slaved to manned 'control' aircraft.

Avpro **Arcangel UCAV**

Top

Underside

Front

Side

Back

ÅVPRO

Despite the continual leaps in UAV technology, the confidence to fly robot air vehicles with weapons on board over friendly forces is just not there at present. Even with self-destruct devices and advanced GPS (Global Positioning System) for pinpoint navigation, it will be decades before the pilot is redundant, if ever.

>>> Insect Repellent <<<

The future of unmanned air vehicles is dividing into two very different technology streams. One is directed to the relatively large, stealthy URAV and UCAV which are required to fulfil roles presently carried out by manned combat aircraft. The other stream is focusing on the other end of the spectrum, the micro-UAV.

One of the most successful and versatile species in history is the insect and micro-technology now makes it possible to produce large numbers of low-cost Robobugs equipped with multiple sensors and capable of undertaking clandestine surveillance and reconnaissance missions.

A future scenario, that a few years ago would have been in the realms of pure science fiction, could be a reality within a decade. The sight of a large insect hovering outside the fifth storey window of a Ministry of Defence building draws little attention from the operators within the building as they focus on their computer screens. It flies slowly from window to window until it finds one open. The dragonfly-like creature then drones its way into the office flying close to the high ceiling. It takes only a few seconds to find its bearings before it zooms out through an open door to the long anonymous corridor outside. Locked in its tiny brain is a complete floor plan of building and it is homing in on a particular location - the Army's operations room. Here the Robobug scans documents, wallcharts, maps and computer screens with its 'eyes', a high-resolution colour video camera relaying the data back to its controller in real time. If commanded, it will inject a virus into one of the network computers. Its mission is completed.

>>> Fantasy or fact? <<<

The fact is that in a very few years time, a family of highly capable Robobugs, which will be cheap, expendable and extremely difficult to detect, will be the outcome of a billion dollar DARPA programme. DARPA's mission statement is: 'To help maintain US technology superiority and guard against unforeseen technological advances by potential adversaries. Consequently, the DARPA mission is to develop imaginative, innovative and often high-risk research ideas offering a significant technological impact that will go well beyond the normal evolutionary development approaches; and pursue these ideas from the demonstration of technical feasibility through to the development of prototype systems.' The Robobug fits will have his own mechanical 'bird' to provide him with images, sounds and even smells of what is inside a target building or vehicle. As part of the DARPA programme, small micro-UAVs, the size of a humming bird or large butterfly, are already a reality. Lockheed Martin's 5 in wingspan *MicroStar*, the similar size AeroVironment *Black Widow* and the UK's *D'Spyfly* are close reconnaissance Micro-UAV prototypes but resemble a freesbie rather than an insect. Below that scale, as birds and insects figured out long ago, the game is played very differently. In fact mechanical engineers can prove that dragonflies cannot possibly fly!

Although insects have been around for millions of years, very little is known about their flight characteristics and it is only now that micro-technology engineers, rather than biologists, are trying to discover the secrets of their flight, and replicate it. What has been discovered is that insects use interacting wing techniques to stay in the air - delayed stall, rotational circulation and wake capture. Future nano-technology has to reproduce these techniques if the Robobug is to become a reality.

Above: Futuristic Joint-Wing UCAVs undertaking a long-range stategic bombing mission, their only protection being speed and stealth.

Also part of DARPA's programme is a $600,000 contract with the University of Toronto to develop a 6 in ornithopter Micro UAV powered by electrostrictive polymer artificial muscles while the Vanderbilt University is working on mimicking the insects' flight mechanism using piezoelectric actuators to resonate metallic structured 'wings'. AeroVironment, with the California's Institute of Technology (CIT) and the Office of Naval Research, has also been awarded a $1.8 million contract to study the possibility of flying a 10 gm flapping 'microbat' that could carry miniature microphone arrays for acoustic homing on sounds.

Other research teams utilising micro-electro-mechanical systems (MEMS) are working on the development of 'smart dust' that will package sensors, communicators and computing power on tiny specks of silicon. The Royal Institute of Technology in Stockholm, Sweden, has built a 1 cm prototype Robobug which is made up from a layer of silicon coated on a membrane. Grooves are cut into the membrane and filled with a plastic material and micro-heaters. When current is altered, the plastic shrinks or expands causing the grooves to bend and activate 'legs' allowing the insect to walk or even land upside down. Activating the wings is, however, more of a problem. Even to create a vehicle with a 6 in wingspan weighing only 4 oz and able to operate autonomously for up to 30 minutes, requires a 7gm DC brush motor delivering 4,000 milliwatts of power using a 26 gm lithium battery. The gearbox, propeller, control actuators and airframe together account for only another 8 gm, while its payload is made up of a 1 gm receiver, a 3 gm downlink transmitter, a 1 gm magnetic compass and a 2 gm black and white video camera!

The AeroVironment *Black Widow* has an airspeed indicator, micro GPS and a colour video camera. The lithium batteries will be soon replaced by a solid oxide fuel cell that will have 2 - 3 times the energy output. The Robobug will have a body made of super-thin stainless steel, wings of mylar and numerous microscopic moving parts including 1 mm diameter gyroscopes. The 'bug' will draw on the sun for power through micro solar panels on its body which can be stored in micro batteries.

Above: UCAV designs resembling animal and birds could be reduced to the size of insects in the very near future.

Although initially the Micro-UAV's role was viewed as part of a conventional battlefield, it did not take long to recognise the fact that it could be extremely helpful in an increasingly common and deadly environment for the modern soldier - the urban battlefield of the third world, so-called peacekeeping operations, and unconventional warfare. A typical mission scenario may include the checking of a building for a sniper using its video cameras and infra-red (IR) sensors or detecting sophisticated booby-traps by sniffing explosives. Other roles could include searching for survivors of a bombing raid with acoustic and heat sensors and which would involve them 'flying' or 'crawling' through the debris of collapsed buildings. Every platoon leader, or even individual soldiers, can carry a clip of expendable Robobugs that will cost only a few dollars to produce.

These are the first of a series of incredible developments of future Robobugs which one day may land on your computer and literally 'suck' out the data, or crawl through the air-conditioning ducts of a 'sealed' control bunker and release a lethal gas killing all inside.

So when you next notice a large 'insect' buzzing your office window - look again!

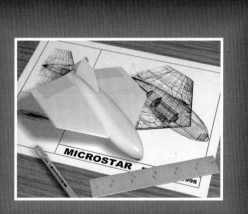

Above: A prototype micro-UAV is Lockheed Martin's composite 5in wingspan MicroStar now undergoing flight trials.

After the end of World War Two, the way ahead for aviation technology was perceived to be a headlong quest for speed. To rule the skies, future warplanes would have to break the sound barrier, fly to the edge of space, and land on conventional runways - and they did. Benefiting from German research and technicians working in America under Operation *Paperclip*, the United States concentrated on rocket-powered experimental aircraft to fly faster and higher.

Germany had produced the first, and only, operational rocket-powered interceptors, the Me 163 *Komet* and Ba 349A *Natter*, and was working on

Above: The world's first, and only operational rocket-powered fighter, was the Messerschmitt Me 163 *Komet*.

Above: Breaking the sound-barrier in level flight was first acheived by the rocket-powered Bell X-1 in October 1947.

Above: Although the German Bachem Ba 349 *Natter* was ordered into production by the SS, the rocket-launched intercepter never entered service.

Above: Britain's 'supersonic' Miles M.52 was close to completion when the Bell X-1 broke the sound-barrier inthe Unitied States.

a Mach 2.0 rocket-powered research aircraft, the DFS 346. Both were later to be developed in the Soviet Union from captured data, the former by Mikoyan as the MiG 1-270, and the latter by OKB-2, manned by former DFS engineers. After disappointing trials in the late 1940s, the Soviet Union abandoned rocket-powered aircraft.

The United States did not. The bullet-shaped, rocket-powered Bell X-1 is credited with making the first true supersonic (Mach 1.0) flight in a climb on 14 October 1947. It was the first of a series of record breaking rocket-powered research aircraft operated by the National Advisory Committee for Aeronautics (NACA), and later the National Aeronautical and Space Administration (NASA) that culminated with the incredible North American X-15, which extended manned flight to more than 4,500 mph (Mach 6.72) and to an altitudes of more than 350,000 ft. Nearly 40 years on, the X-15 remains the world's fastest manned aircraft.

In Europe, Britain had been on the brink of flying a supersonic rocket-powered aircraft when

Above: The British Saunders-Roe SR.53 was an innovative mixed power aircraft using a rocket for climb and a jet for cruise.

Below: The prototype for the proposed SR.177 mixed-power interceptor ordered by the post-war *Luftwaffe,* the SR-53 was successfully flight tested before being cancelled in 1957.

Below: Already operating on the edge of space are a new generation of unmanned 'atmospheric satellites' such as the all-copsite HALO-Proteus.

the X-1 broke the sound barrier in 1947. One third scale models of the Miles M.52 dropped from 'mother' aircraft had reached the speed of Mach 1.35. The Royal Aircraft Establishment (RAE) Transonic Research Programme called for an aircraft that would fly at 1,000 mph at 36,000 ft and reach that height in 1 1/2 minutes.

The innovative M.52 had a bi-convex wing section, a slab tailplane, power controls and a pressurised capsule cockpit. It was designed to be powered by a three-stage after-burning ducted fan jet engine but, due to rising costs, the project was cancelled in 1947 before making its first flight. Both Britain and France experimented with mixed rocket/jet-powered

aircraft in the 1950s, with the SO 6025 *Espadon* becoming the first French level-supersonic aircraft in 1953.

As a technology demonstrator for a mixed power-plant interceptor, the British Saunders-Roe SR.53 made several successful test fights between 1957-9 using a jet engine for cruising and a rocket motor for climb performance and Mach 2.0 in level flight. The projected production fighter, the SR.177, was cancelled in 1957, again before it was completed.

Although incredible high speeds and altitudes were attained by rocket-powered aircraft, most of them had to be carried aloft by a 'mother' launch aircraft and had a full-power endurance measured only in minutes. With the increasing power, efficiency and economy of second generation jet engines, rocket-powered aircraft were all but abandoned by the 1960s although they remained vital for space exploration. However, another German wartime project, the hypersonic rocket-powered Sanger-Bredt Stratospheric Bomber remained an unfulfilled dream. Powered by a 100 tonne thrust rocket motor with a duration of 10 minutes, the craft would be launched from a rocket-powered sled, accelerate to Mach 18 at an altitude of nearly 500,000 ft to give it maximum range of almost 15,000 miles. It would then skim through the atmosphere to glide down to land on a conventional airfield. It was one of Germany's more bizarre concepts, born out of desperation. But six decades later, atmosphere-skimming hypersonic aircraft are about to become a reality.

Both the Gulf War and the Balkans campaigns highlighted a shortfall in the USAF's strike/reconnaissance capability and it is looking into space to address some of these concerns. In 1999, US Air Force Space Command doubled its space-related research budget to $320 million to develop a series of rapid-reaction strike space craft, reusable launch

Above: Before 1990, the Soviet Union was close to deploying 'edge-of space' long-range strategic bombers such as the Myansishchyev M-20.

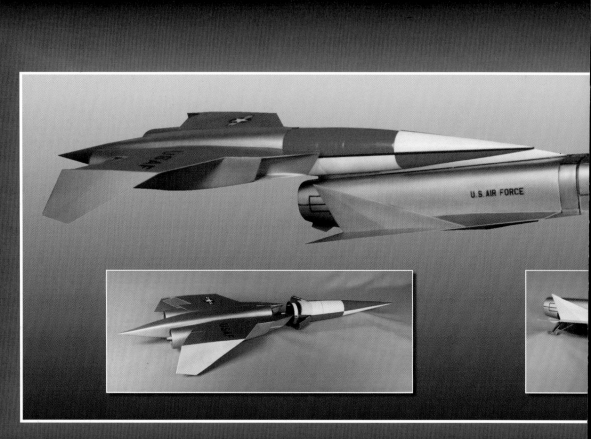

Above: An early 'edge-of space' surveillance platform was the GD Super Hustler designed in the late 1950s to be air-launched by a B-58 bomber. A jet-booster (inset left) accelerated the manned vehicle (inset right) to ramjet speeds of Mach 6.25 at 125,000 feet.

vehicles (RLV) and Space Based Laser (SBL) systems to be used for the detection and destruction of theatre ballistic missiles and advanced cruise missile threats. Several of these projects can trace their roots back to programmes implemented during President Reagan's Strategic Defense Initiative (SDI) in the 1980s, which brought the Soviet Union to its knees as vast amounts of money were pumped into US Ballistic Missile Defense (BMD) projects, although most of them never progressed beyond the concept stage.

Research from SDI has been fed into the USAF's Airborne Laser programme, which uses a modified Boeing 747 airframe fitted with a megawatt-class laser system. The AL-1's mission will be to destroy theatre ballistic missiles while they are still over the launch area. USAF AL-1As will operate autonomously while cruising at over 40,000 ft, hundreds of miles away from its target with wide-angle infra-Red (IR) sensors providing 360° coverage.

In order to maintain and safeguard vital defence communications in the future, new secure stratospheric relay platforms will also have to be developed. Leading the race for a practical and affordable option is Angel Technologies' High-Altitude Long-Operation (HALO) *Proteus* system, which uses an all-composite canard configured twin-jet unmanned aircraft. The Scaled Composites' *Proteus* will orbit 60,000 ft above a major city or operations theatre for up to 18 hours, providing a secure satellite communications network over an area 100 miles in diameter.

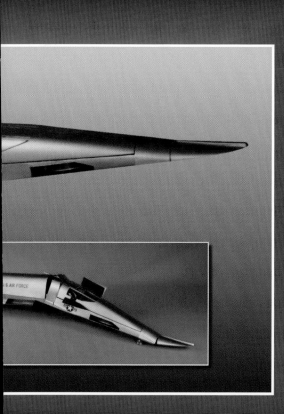

Northrop Grumman is proposing a similar high-altitude relay system based on its *Global Hawk* high-altitude long-endurance UAV carrying a military airborne communication node.

At the beginning of the 21st century, the airship is also going into space, or its fringes. The unmanned High-Altitude Long-Endurance (HALE) airship designed by the UK-based Lindstrand Balloons and Germany's DiamlerChrysler Aerospace will be unique in that it will be solar-powered. Thanks to the development of cheap flexible solar cells that can produce power for the airship's computers, a payload that is capable of handling up to 100,000 communication simultaneously and electric engines, the HALE could be a practical relay system. The 600 ft-long composite constructed helium-filled aerostat would operate at 70,000 ft where there is no weather, few winds and little humidity.

Below: Future hypersonic strike aircraft may be powered to Mach 25.0 by Pulse Detonation Wave Engines (PDWE) augmented with Magnetohydrdynamic (MHD) fan propulsion and plasma spikes.

Above: The Linear Aerospike SR-71 Experiment (LASRE) flight testing a new propulsion system for future hypersonic aircraft.

Lockheed Martin's Skunk Works is involved in providing system integration for yet another solar-powered communication-relay airship, the *Sky Station*. Designed by the UK's Airship Technologies company, the project has international backing and plans to launch its stratospheric communications service using 500 ft-long aerostats in geo-stationary positions at 70,000 ft, in 2003.

>>> Space Wars <<<

The future of the USAF's space-based hypersonic strike/reconnaissance platforms rests on the successful development of new propulsion systems. While conventional rocket motors can provide the power required for hypersonic flight, they require literally tons of fuel for any reasonable endurance.

Boeing's Phantom Works is already working with NASA on the development of the X-43 Hyper-X, designed to fly beyond Mach 7.0 on air-breathing propulsion, a Supersonic-Combustion RamJet - known as the Scramjet. If successful, Hyper-X will be the first 'White' programme, air-breathing winged aircraft to achieve hypersonic speed.

One report that confirms the viability of a hypersonic aircraft, was published in 1997 by the Phantom Works which stated that a scramjet-powered B-1 sized aircraft could achieve Mach 10 with a 10,000 lb payload and have a radius of action in the region of 5,000 miles plus.

The USAF's HySet programme sets out to develop technology for hypersonic Mach 25 space vehicles with a Rocket-Based Combined Cycle (RBCC) system, powered craft using both air-breathing scramjets and pure rocket motors. The engineering concept developed by the Lawrence Livermore National Laboratory in California is known as *HyperSoar*, a hypersonic strike aircraft that would 'skip' on the upper atmosphere to enable it to reach any position over the Earth's surface in less than two hours from take-off.

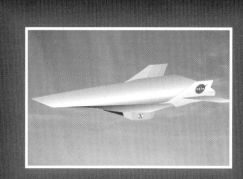

Above: A model of the Scramjet-powered Hyper-X craft being developed by the Boeing Phantom Works.

The projected 200 ft-long wedge-shaped *HyperSoar* could carry a 100,000 lb payload over a range of 6,000 miles cruising at Mach 10. Capable of taking off from a 10,000 ft-long conventional runway, it would use its scramjets to accelerate to Mach 10 while climbing to 115,000 ft where its RBCC system would be shut down as it enters orbit. The craft would then continue to climb to some 200,000 ft under its own momentum before beginning a gentle descent to a lower altitude, between 115,000-132,000 ft, where the engines would fire again for some 20 seconds. The wedge-shaped 'waverider' would literally surf through the air on its own shockwave.

HyperSoar's military potential is obvious. A small fleet of these craft could move men and equipment to trouble-spots anywhere in the world within hours of an outbreak of hostilities, as well as carry out strategic surveillance missions to fill the gap left by the premature retirement of the SR-71 *Blackbird*. It would also have a global strike capability which would enable it to carry out a precision first strike at speeds and

Above: The Mach 7.0 X-43 Hyper-X will be the first air-breathing winged craft to acheive hypersonic speed.

Above: Wave-riding laser-equipped UCAVs deployed to the upper atmosphere could become integral parts of the USAF Ballistic Missile Defense (BMD) programme.

altitudes that would be far beyond any known air defences, thus eliminating the need for large escort packages that are required for a typical USAF B-2A intercontinental bombing mission.

A successor to the cruise missile being designed by the Boeing Phantom Works powered by a hydrogen-fuelled scramjet could be in service by 2010. Developed under the US Defense Advanced Research Projects Agency's Affordable Rapid-Response Missile Demonstrator (ARRMD) programme, the air-launched missile will climb to 100,000 ft at Mach 6.5 and cover 500 miles in seven minutes.

If, and when, the RBCC propulsion system is proved to be a practicality, even more advanced developments will be in the NASA pipeline. Grouped under the Hybrid Hyperspeed Propulsion (HHP) programme for perfecting air-breathing technology for space vehicles along with the RBCC, is the Pulse Detonation Engine (PDE) which has been selected to be taken to a demonstration phase under NASA's REVCON (Revolutionary Concepts) programme.

The PDE is based on the pulse-jet that was pioneered by Germany's Argus Motorenwerke in the 1930s and used to power the World War Two V-1 'Doodlebug' flying bomb. In its simplest form, it is a tube through which a compressed air/fuel mixture is exploded. A sub-scale PDE will be flown on a NASA SR-71 before a full-scale system, which would comprise a number of tubes to provide constant thrust, would be constructed and tested.

Other HHP programme vehicles include the *Stargazer*, a small wedge-shaped launch vehicle, similar in design to *HyperSoar*, powered by four Scramjet RBCC systems, and the simpler wing-body *Starsabre* concept which would use only two Ramjet RBCCs.

While the REVCON programme is focussed on the long term future, present technology is occupied with the design of second generation Reusable Launch Vehicles (RLV) to replace the US Shuttle. The most ambitious programme is Lockheed Martin's Single-Stage-to-Orbit (SSTO) *VentureStar* which is a large lifting-body to be vertically launched using Linear Aerospike propulsion systems. The X-33 is designed to reach Mach 12 and an altitude of 250,000 ft during trials in 2005 when powered by the Boeing Rocketdyne XRS-2200. However, the first in-flight trials of the engine system mounted on the back of a NASA SR-71, known as Linear Aerospike SR-71 Experiment (LASRE), were less successful than had been anticipated and this situation added to the fact that costs are constantly escalating. The time scale of the *VentureStar* programme is now in doubt.

A more conventional low-cost RLV programme is the air-launched Orbital Sciences X-34 powered by a conventional Fastrec liquid oxygen/kerosene- fuelled rocket motor designed to ferry six-man teams or small equipment payloads to space stations. A demonstrator vehicle made its first unpowered glide flight at the end of 1999 released from a high flying OSC *TriStar* carrier aircraft.

Above: A forerunner of Reusable Launch Vehicles (RLV), the rocket-powered Martin-Marietta X-24B lifting body glides to earth during a 1970s test flight.

Europe had an excellent opportunity to take the lead in the race to produce a viable SSTO. In 1987, British Aerospace proposed a Horizontal Take-Off and Landing (HOTOL) Reusable Launch Vehicle (RLV) powered by a revolutionary new propulsion system. The Rolls-Royce RBB545 Swallow was a combined air-breathing jet/hydrogen-oxygen rocket engine. HOTOL's 200 ft-long cylindrical fuselage had a long slender delta-wing developed from *Concorde*, originally designed by German scientist Dietrich Kuchman who was part of the UK's equivalent of Operation *Paperclip*.

Designed to take off from a 7,500 ft-long runway at a speed of 325 mph, HOTOL would reach Mach 5.0 in eight minutes, at which time a steep rocket-powered climb would be initiated. When orbital velocity was achieved, the engine is cut-off and the craft would soar up to an operating altitude of some 200 miles carrying a 14,000 payload. Manoeuvring in space would be controlled by an Orbital Manoeuvring System (OMS) and HOTOL would re-enter the Earth's atmosphere to make a conventional glide-landing in the same way as the Shuttle.

Despite promising research, the UK was then a junior member of the European Space Agency (ESA) and was in competition with the French *Hermes* mini-shuttle, and the German *Sangar* – a name from the past, two-stage launch

Above: The concept demonstrator for a future Russian 'space-fighter', the Mikoyan *Spirel*, was the unmanned POB-2 lifting body vehicle.

vehicle. Due to lack of British government commitment, the promising HOTOL never progressed beyond the concept stage. Neither did either of its rivals and the ESA's Future Launchers Technology Programme (FLTP) is still studying several European RLV concepts but suffers from a lack of sufficient funding.

Further down the development line is NASA's X-38A, a lift body vehicle designed as a six-seat autonomous escape system for the crew of the International Space Station. Sub-scale test vehicles of the Crew Return Vehicle (CRV), which will be guided by a Satellite Navigation System (SNS) to land on conventional runways using steerable aerofoils, have made a series of free-flight tests after release from a NASA B-52.

The lifting body design of the X-38, which was developed from the earlier Martin Marietta X-24A, closely resembles an unmanned test vehicle for the Soviet *Uragan* (Hurricane) program. The *Uragan* was conceived as a two-crew 'Shuttle-killer' armed with a recoilless gun and launched into space by a Zenith rocket booster. A sub-scale unmanned BOR-4 made a series of orbital test flights in the 1980s, one of which ended in the Indian Ocean, before the programme was cancelled in 1987.

Although President Reagan's Strategic Defense Initiative (SDI) was never implemented, a 'Son of Star Wars' programme is being studied in which ground tracking stations located worldwide and orbiting tracking satellites would be able to detect the infrared (IR) heat signature of ballistic missiles and relay the information to US air defence headquarters. The programme calls for up to 100 hypersonic anti-missile interceptors to be based in Alaska to provide an anti-missile umbrella for the US mainland.

The Royal Air Force and the UK Defence Evaluation and Research Agency (DERA) is also studying the feasibility of developing an independent missile shield to cover the United Kingdom and possibly continental Europe as part of their Technology, Readiness and Risk Assessment Programme (TRAPP). More than a dozen computer-simulated 'what if' war game scenarios are being evaluated with a report scheduled to be issued in 2001 which may recommend that the UK joins the US 'Son of Star Wars' programme (it joined the original SDI in 1985) or to go it alone.

One of the USAF Space Command's intentions is to deploy additional command, control, communications and computers (C4) and surveillance satellites equipped with electro-optics (EO), space-based synthetic aperture radar (SAR) and hyper-spectral imaging which may become part of the 'Son of Star Wars programme. These may well become tempting targets for other nations and although the Air Force plans to fly clusters of integrated satellites to maximise their survivability, it will require vehicles to service and protect them.

The USAF would like to have a capability to launch and recover a vehicle from the ground, that can fly at the edge of space, well out of range of any modern Surface-to-Air Missile (SAM) systems, to target ground

Above: Another space-based Phantom Works programme is the developent of USAF's X-40A, an unmanned multi-mission Space Maneuver Vehicle (SMV).

targets or air targets such as cruise and *Scud* missiles or long-range bombers, with advanced diode-pumped solid-state megawatt lasers.

Taking a step into space operations, the USAF has funded the X-40A Space Manoeuvre Vehicle (SMV) programme. Designed to be launched into orbit by an Expendable Launch Vehicle (ELV) or 'piggy back' on a sub-orbital Space Operations Vehicle (SOV), to remain in orbit for up to a year and to manoeuvre to inspect other spacecraft, the SMV will pave the way for a larger Trans-Atmospheric Vehicle (TAV) that will explore the technology for both a ŠSTO military spacecraft and a hypersonic strike/reconnaissance vehicle.

These may be a bi-product of NASA's HHP and REVCON programmes and the dream or nightmare of the World War Two Sanger-Bredt Stratospheric Bomber project, which was launched on a sled from a five mile track, may become a reality almost a century on. The Magnetic Levitation, or Maglev, track launch system may give a space launch vehicle a 'running start' to enable it to break free from Earth's gravity. The system would use magnetic fields to levitate a sled carrying the space vehicle and accelerate it along a track at speeds of up to 600 mph. The vehicle would then fire its rocket engines for launch to orbit.

Looking even further into the future, a true hyper-velocity air-rider capable of speeds in access of Mach 25 combines SDI research with that of Russia's Academy of Sciences. The revolutionary Aero-Lens vehicle, will be powered by a silent PDE to accelerate it to supersonic speeds within the dense air of low altitude or the rarefied atmosphere of lower orbit. At this point magnetohydrodynamic (MHD) fan propulsion would literally explode the air around the rim of the vehicle and blast it to a velocity of Mach 25+. A plasma spike, developed by the same Russian research centre, uses concentrated microwave energy projected forward of the Aero-Lens to burn through the dense air from its path. At these velocities, the Aero-Lens would enable a manned or unmanned vehicle to arrive on target anywhere on globe within minutes, rather than hours, of launch.

Many innovative space research programmes were embarked on by Soviet Union although they became focused on a quest for ever larger, more powerful space rocket launchers in the 1960s. Some of these were directed to RLV research. In the mid-1960s, the famed Mikoyan design bureau begun work on a future 'Space-Fighter'. The *Spirel* was a Two-Stage-To-Orbit (TSTO) vehicle comprising a Mach 6.0 air-breathing jet-powered 'mother' craft that would carry a detachable piloted orbital lift body craft to an altitude of 100,000 ft to launch it into space. It would re-enter the atmosphere and land on a conventional runway. Its main roles were that of strike/reconnaissance, to search for and destroy 'enemy' space vehicles, but the project was cancelled following the Soviet Union's decision to develop its own space shuttle, the *Buran*, after a technology demonstrator of the orbital craft had made a series of successful test flights.

This was one of many projects inspired by the Soviet Union's perceived threat from the America's B-70 hypersonic strategic bomber that was designed to operate on the threshold of space. This began with USAF's WS (Weapons System) -110A programme in the mid-1950s for a supersonic nuclear bomber for Strategic Air Command (SAC) and resulted in the North American XB-60 *Valkyrie* that made its first flight in September 1964.

The specification called for the bomber to fly at heights of 100,000 ft, cruise at Mach 2.0 with Mach 3.0 'dash' capability, and have an unrefuelled range of 6,000 miles. A year after its first flight, the 189 ft-long delta-winged *Valkyrie* achieved a sustained speed of Mach 3.0. After only two aircraft were built, one of which was destroyed in a mid-air collision with a NASA F-104 flown by X-15 test pilot Joe Walker who died in the June 1966 accident, the over-cost programme was cancelled. But this was not before the Soviets had embarked on a number of advanced and extremely expensive programmes to counter the B-70 threat including the '*Valkyrie*-killer' MiG-25 *Foxbat*, and its own hypersonic strategic bomber, the Myasishchyev M-15 *Bounder*, which was cancelled soon after the B-70.

Two decades later, the Mikoyan bureau designed another hypersonic strike/reconnaissance craft, designated the MiG-301. Powered by two scramjets, the Mach 4 aircraft was to be the Russian Air Force's 'sixth' generation combat aircraft while the Tupolev bureau began work on a complementary hypersonic strategic bomber. Powered by eight liquid hydrogen fuelled scramjets combined with rocket motors, similar to the US RBCC propulsion system, the giant 330 ft-long Tu-2000 had a projected payload of 330,000 lb and would cruise at Mach 6 at 100,000 ft. However, since the break-up of the Soviet Union, both of these projects have remained on the drawing board.

Above: Designed as a six-man space rescue vehicle, to operate from conventional runways, the Orbital Sciences X-34
is powered by a liquide-oxygen/kerosene powered rocket motor.

All of Russia's space technology and budget has been directed towards the design and construction of the
International Space Station but with the election of a new hard-line president in early 2000, there are signs
that future co-operative ventures may be curtailed and additional funds will be directed to 'State' space